Health Service Counselling

WILLIAM STEWART

Senior Nursing Officer (Allocation),
Southampton University Hospitals
Combined School of Nursing

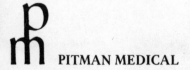

PITMAN MEDICAL

First published 1979

Catalogue Number 21 3470 81

Pitman Medical Publishing Co Ltd
P O Box 7, Tunbridge Wells,
Kent, TN1 1XH, England

Associated Companies

UNITED KINGDOM
Pitman Publishing Ltd, London
Focal Press Ltd, London

CANADA
Copp Clark Pitman, Toronto

USA
Fearon Pitman Publishers Inc, San Francisco
Focal Press Inc, New York

AUSTRALIA
Pitman Publishing Pty Ltd, Melbourne

NEW ZEALAND
Pitman Publishing NZ Ltd, Wellington

British Library Cataloguing in Publication Data

Stewart, William, b.1927
    Health service counselling.
    1. Counseling—Great Britain   2. Medical
    care — Great Britain
    I   Title
    362.1'0425   BF637.C6

    ISBN 0-272-79552-6

Set in 11/12 pt IBM Journal by
Gatehouse Wood Ltd, Cowden, Kent
Printed by offset-lithography and bound
in Great Britain at The Pitman Press, Bath

Contents

To the many people whose relationships have enriched my experience from which I have freely drawn.

Preface

The basic premise of this book is that everyone in the health services has a counselling function. When I speak of 'health services', I do not mean only those employed within the National Health Service, for there are many other people, doctors and nurses in the Occupational Health field and in private practice whom I would not wish to exclude by limiting what I have to say to employees of the N.H.S.

There are those who counsel effectively and there are those who do not; there are many who wish they could, and feel they should, but also feel they lack the necessary skill. If you are already an experienced counsellor what I say may open some new doors for you. If you never counsel, is it because you feel it is not part of your role? If that is your view, I would ask you to read on and see if you modify your opinion.

What I have written is for you, the reader who feels he *should* counsel but is not sure where to start. I hope after reading through the book you will realise that counselling is not mysterious or alarming but is an exciting and rewarding experience.

I would not presume to suggest that by reading this book you will have at your finger-tips all that it takes to be an effective counsellor, but it would be a starting point. A careful study of the principles outlined here will provide a basis for counselling practice. Nothing succeeds like success, and what you read must be put into practice. Counselling draws on experience rather than on specific knowledge and you can only gain this experience by counselling.

"Counselling is not simply a matter of applying techniques and principles which have been learned, but it is a process which demands a high degree of self-awareness, an ability to establish relationships and to analyse your own part in the counselling process."*

This analytical acumen derives from a critical combination of personality coupled with training and experience. The innate qualities of personality, training or experience alone will not be sufficient to develop the depth of sensitivity and awareness essential for counselling to be productive. Personality is the foundation, training the superstructure and experience the stones which are carefully and painstakingly laid in developing the counsellor. The aim of this book is to enable you to stand back and take a new look at these three integral and related factors which influence your approach to counselling. I would urge all who accept counselling as part of their role to seek out some form of training that will provide the framework around which their counselling skills can develop.

I hope that the principles expounded in this book will be applicable to those who are directly concerned in patient care; those who have a management or teaching function as well as students within any of the health service professions.

Some of the time I will refer to 'client' meaning the person being counselled, for this is an accepted term in counselling practice. At other times 'counsellee' will be used; generally this will be when a manager is doing the counselling. I hope this will cater for all readers.

WILLIAM STEWART
Bishopstoke 1979

---

* Reprinted from 'Tackling an Insidious Disease', by William Stewart. Published in *Health & Social Services Journal,* 21 October, 1977.

Foreword

The author of this interesting little book on the place of counselling in management is an allocations officer with an area health authority. He is, therefore, not only a nurse but an experienced manager—not unexpectedly he writes to reconcile the two roles.

Interest shown by nurses in the health problems of organisational settings is not exactly new. One hundred years ago a nurse, with a beautiful name which now escapes me, set up the first occupational health service in England. In more recent times health and social services have been deeply affected by rapid organisational growth and change. This has led to many counsellors being moved into management away from direct contact with clients. This book reveals how one such counsellor, a nurse, thinks of himself as manager/counsellor. It seems clear to him that one can care as well as manage. We who are at the receiving end of the health services, traditionally see nurses as being skilled in the delivery of a cool, competent and caring service—delivered without fuss or unnecessary intrusion. The author of this book feels strongly that nurses and indeed all who have caring roles within organisations, should themselves be cared for.

While social practitioners have thus been acquiring management skills, there has at the same time been an increasing interest shown by industry generally in counselling as a legitimate management activity. In fact, it occurred to me, when reading this book, that if the illustrations used had not been so evidently from a hospital, it could well be a book about an industrial organisation. Most of the matters discussed have general application and could be of use to any manager seeking to understand people better. Stress is difficult to define. To the counsellor stress is real. This rare account of how it feels to encounter stress while counselling within an organisation is a valuable contribution to the debate on management styles.

JOHN LIGHTBODY
Employee Counsellor
Shell Chemicals UK Ltd
December, 1978

ACKNOWLEDGEMENTS

My thanks must go first to my erstwhile colleague Liz Burrows whose razor-sharp brain cut through much of my untidy tangle. Secondly to Bill Burnett of Wessex Region whose encouragement kept me going. Lastly to my family whose patience has been a source of inspiration.

NOTE ON INDEXING

Some books, by the nature of the subjects, cry out for an index; for others an index is less essential. Some never have an index at all: this is one such book.

The purpose of an index is to provide the reader with a quick reference to topics and ideas; a "Where on earth did I read that" situation. For factual information and complicated data it is useful to refer to specific pages. There is, however, the point that sometimes the 'wholeness' of the book is destroyed if the reader is tempted to use the index to 'dip into', titillated by a word taken at random (and possibly out of context) rather than absorb the total message.

What I *have* done is to provide detailed chapter headings which should act as a guide to the contents as well as being a reference.

You may like to consider the advantage of constructing your own reference section by jotting ideas and thoughts as you come to them, on the blank pages provided. These notes, *because they are specific to you* will be of more benefit than a list of words which *I* think are essential.

PART 1

The Process

CHAPTER 1

The Individual Within the Organisation

THE PATIENT AS COUNSELLEE

Competent to Counsel?

The main theme of this book is that many people are expected to counsel as part of their role. This applies very much to nurses. They are approached by people for help, merely because they are known to be nurses. This implies that they are expected to be competent to counsel, but training as a nurse does not automatically make one competent to counsel. One of the facets of any counselling is dealing with the unexpected—on the spot, the spur of the moment situation; this implies an ever-ready attitude which lends itself to all that counselling implies.

I have chosen to commence this book with a patient, because patients are central to any health service. This situation could have arisen anywhere where nurse and patient meet, and the fact that I have placed the situation within a hospital in no way implies that hospital nurses are any more competent to counsel than others in the health services. The person could just as well have been a physiotherapist, laboratory technician or a domestic: she just happened to be there at the right time.

The Situation

Mr Ian Andrews, a man of 40 years, was admitted to a medical ward by his G.P. for investigations. He had been complaining of 'palpitations', racing pulse and tightness over the chest. The G.P. had thoroughly examined him and could find nothing amiss: an E.C.G. showed no abnormality. Mr Andrews was very anxious and his symptoms persisted in spite of sedation.

Staff Nurse Simpson was on duty when Mr Andrews arrived. When he was in bed he called her over; she noticed his pallor and sweating hands.

[A = responses by Mr Andrews; S = responses by Staff Nurse]

A 1 Nurse, please take my pulse, I've got these strange feelings, my heart's thumping like mad and my chest feels tight.

S 1 (taking pulse) Yes, Mr Andrews, it does seem a little bit faster than average. Do you know what your normal rate is? [Positive reassurance. It would do little to reassure the patient by saying his pulse rate was normal or "There is nothing to worry about".]

A 2 Usually about 70. Now it's about 100.

S 2 Not quite; about 86. How long have you had these feelings? [This may not seem 'right' to some—to give the rate—but she obviously believed in being 'honest' and that this would allay his anxieties. After all the patient could count it for himself. She asks a question which, although still connected, takes the focus off the pulse.]

A 3 For some time now, but I only went to the doctor last week, when I woke one night with these dreadful feelings. You might not believe this, but I thought I'd had my chips.

S 3 You were frightened? [Focussing on feelings.]

A 4 Dead scared. That's funny, 'dead scared', scared of being dead I suppose. I live alone—my wife and I have separated, I'm not on the phone. I was rooted to the bed, I can tell you.

S.4 How long did it last?

A 5 *It seemed like all night, but I don't suppose it was. Do you think it's a coronary?*

S 5 *I expect you wondered that at the time?* [She could have answered this with a 'yes' or 'no' or evaded it by saying "You'll have to ask the doctor". She could have given an opinion or she could have evaded it. What would you have done? Instead she chose to concentrate on his feelings by getting him to answer his own question.]

A 6 *Yes I did and still do. If it's not that it must be something else wrong with my heart, mustn't it?*

S 6 *Well, of course it could be and that's why you're here, to find out, but palpitations do not always mean heart disease. In a way it's like sitting for an exam. When I had my viva I had severe palpitations and* . . [interruption].

A 7 *Are you saying it's my nerves?* [He had obviously taken exception to the link she appeared to be trying to make between his 'heart' condition and her 'exam nerves'.]

S 7 *No, what I mean is that it's the body's response to some stress. In my case the exam; in others it could be overwork, bereavement or something like that.*

A 8 [Pause] *Sorry nurse, I jumped at you then, didn't I?* [apologetic smile]. *Somebody at work said it was my nerves and I thought you were saying the same thing. How can stress cause something like this?*

(Here she explained to him the fight and flight responses of the body, again using the illustration of the exam. As he talked, she realised that there was a strong undercurrent of anxiety linked with his broken marriage on account of which he had thrown himself more into his work.)

A 9 *You know, nurse, I'm beginning to feel better already* [he took his own pulse]. *Yes, it's slowed down and some of the tightness has gone. Thank you for talking to me. Can I talk with you again if I feel like I did just now?*

There is nothing dramatic about this incident; a nurse going about her work-a-day tasks; no cloistered interview, just a chat by a bedside. But counselling it certainly was. One person helping another through a difficult patch: helping him to gain insight, understanding of some part of his problem, bringing a sense of well-being and stability. This, in a nutshell, is what counselling is, no matter where or for what purpose.

WHAT IS STAFF COUNSELLING?

Staff counselling is counselling a member of staff because of some problem associated with work. There is nothing intrinsically different between counselling a staff member with a work problem and counselling someone with a marital problem—the only difference is in the focus. The process is the same although the problem is different.

A definition of staff counselling is: helping a member of staff achieve an adjustment either within himself or within his environment. This adjustment may be between two members of a family—husband and wife, parent and child—between boss and subordinate, two members of staff, or student and tutor. The problem may also arise between the staff member and some aspect of his work; some adjustment is necessary if he is to function effectively.

A point of view held by some is that managers should only become involved in counselling when the specific problem clearly arises at work and that they cannot become involved in what happens away from work. I cannot subscribe to this view. I believe that:

> . . . to concentrate on what a man *does* to the exclusion of what he *is*, is like trying to separate the white of an egg from the yolk. It can be done but one is left with something incomplete. Performance, in any field of labour, is influenced by what a man is; what a man is, influences what he does. Counselling must consider the whole man.*

The problem Tom Jenkins† experiences away from work does have a tendency to undermine his working efficiency. Likewise it would be very difficult for Tom to leave behind him all the emotions following a heated confrontation with

---

* Quoted from *A Guide to Counselling*, William Stewart, 1977.
Published by Wessex Regional Health Authority.
† See case study in Part 3.

the laundry manager or someone else at work. How often have we heard it said, "Oh don't bring your work problems home to me" or "Don't bring your problems to work with you"?

It would be true to say that certain problems can be left more easily where the action is. The fact that you are having difficulty with the builders or with the car could be more easily left at home than the knowledge that a loved one suffers from an incurable illness. The difference between these two situations—the car and the loved one—is the degree of emotional involvement. Managers cannot, indeed dare not, ignore, or write off as irrelevant, what happens to their staff in the hours they are not at work. The hours spent at work are only about one-third of the total day, so it is natural that how these other hours are spent must have some bearing on work performance--for good or ill.

So very often we consider this question--how work is influenced by what we do—from a negative standpoint, by looking at the problems created by some difficulty the person is experiencing, that we overlook the positive benefits derived at work by the way a person lives. There can be no doubt that the person who is blessed with congenial, satisfying and interesting social activities and home circumstances, fruitful relationships and good health is more likely to be able to make a positive contribution at work than the person for whom all these aspects are negatively loaded.

If this assumption is correct, it is impossible for managers to ignore the influence of the hours spent away from work *when it comes to considering performance.* I would not go as far as to suggest that the manager should invade the privacy of the individual; neither is it necessary, or possible, for him to participate in, or actively investigate, how his staff spend their time: this would be an unwarranted invasion of personal liberty which would be certain to breed resentment. No, what it does mean is that he must never overlook this aspect of the person's life and its influence on performance.

MANAGEMENT RESOURCES

Managers are primarily concerned with three resources—

7

money, materials and people— and it is how these resources are managed (or mismanaged) which will determine the efficiency of any organisation.

Some managers try to keep these three resources apart—in watertight compartments—and it is certainly true that functional experts have emerged in all these areas and some managers have been very glad to relinquish to them many of the (to them) onerous responsibilities which once bogged them down.

With the development of Personnel departments, managers relinquished many of the functions which now could be dealt with more professionally. An assumption drawn from this, by some if not by all, is that as welfare, officially, became a personnel function so did counselling, which is logically a part of welfare.

Some personnel managers *do* see counselling as part of their role but many do not, and perhaps it is not desirable that staff within one department are seen as the only ones who have counselling skills. Personnel departments are definitely not counselling agencies: that was never the intention. But what has happened, in many instances, is that we have lost the art of dealing with people on a personal level. We need to rediscover how to relate to the people with whom we work and so help to create a working atmosphere where counselling is accepted as natural- as the province of everyone and not of a few or those who belong to special counselling agencies.

I believe that many managers are genuinely seeking ways in which they can gain a better understanding of relationships at work. They regret their inability to deal with their staff who have problems and intuitively recognise that, for staff to give of their best, they must be in harmony. Whenever harmony is disrupted, discord results and relationships cease to be productive where discord reigns.

It would not be overstating the case to say that of the three resources—money, materials and people—it is the understanding of people at a deep personal level—how relationships are established and maintained—which has been sadly neglected over the past decades as we have sought ways to develop other skills related to money and materials.

BALANCING RESOURCES

I do not suggest that the 'people' factor should receive undue attention at the expense of the other two. This was the principal undoing of the human relations approach of a previous era. It is essential to maintain a balance between all three resources if they are to operate smoothly together.

MANAGERS AS COUNSELLORS

If counselling is 'hived off' to a specialist department, or to specialists, it will reduce the ability (and the desire) of the average person to deal with problem-solving. The answer is not to train more specialists but to reverse the process and keep the action where it originates. If every manager has some understanding of counselling—even although some will, by virtue of a match between personality and experience, become more skilled than others—fewer problems will necessitate specialist intervention because they will be solved before they reach breaking point.

Managers who develop skills in counselling find that there are added advantages. Because they become more aware of the factors which make or mar relationships they develop a sensitivity and an awareness which influences their own relationships; this of course applies also to working relationships. I do not want to give the impression that managers who are skilled in counselling are paragons, that they never become annoyed, or say the wrong thing or irritate other people; such people must be as equally difficult to live with as those who are constantly doing battle! If relationships at work are improved as a result of greater understanding it must surely lead to greater efficiency because stress is more likely to be dealt with before it reaches flash point.

It is sometimes argued that people become teachers within their trade or profession because they lack the ability to be first-class practitioners; and similarly people become managers or administrators who are not competent in dealing with relationships. Generalisations are dangerous and this is one of them. There are as many different reasons why people become teachers or managers as there are teachers and managers. But I think it is true that there are many managers who, as I indicated earlier, concentrate on other functions of management and ignore working relationships. I think, too, that there is often the unspoken assumption that because management does involve people the manager will counsel by intuition rather than by training.

I do not belittle intuition; those who have it are blessed indeed. Training in relationships will give the manager a more sure framework within which he can allow his intuition to work. Sometimes people who have been counselling for a number of years, and then become involved in training, feel a loss of confidence as they examine the foundations of their practice.

A person who plays the piano by ear and then takes up serious piano study would find, initially, that his pace would be very slow. He may take a long time to master the combination of reading and playing; even those rhythms and melodies which he had played expertly before seem to elude him. This is because he is having to analyse what he is doing before he can rebuild.

The same thing happened to me when I commenced social work training. Where previously I had relied on intuition I now had to relate what I was doing to theory and structure. For a time I felt that my intuition had deserted me but afterwards I realised that it had become sharper because I was using it as an aid and not as the foundation for counselling practice.

The manager who becomes skilled in counselling will be in a better position to ensure that the wheels of the organisation continue to turn smoothly. The wheels are the three resources, revolving like cogs in a machine, all together, all of equal importance.

STRESS

Within any organisation or industry there are a number of departments each of which has these three resources central to its existence. If one department is not performing efficiently, a degree of stress will be placed on the organisation. If a number of departments are under-functioning, a great deal of stress will result which could lead to serious malfunctioning of the organisation. This is analogous to the human body where each part is interdependent on all others. If one limb is 'out of sorts', the whole body is affected but it can cope: if a large percentage of the body is not functioning properly, the body is put under great stress.

Stress is something which everyone experiences to some degree and must cope with in one way or another. There is, however, a certain level above which stress becomes danger-ous. Car drivers recognise the warning signs of intolerable stress when the temperature gauge begins to creep up and up. When it reaches danger point, unless the car is stopped, the engine will overheat, resulting in permanent damage.

The same thing happens in organisations. Organisations, however, are not hunks of metal like a car, but are living, breathing, vital organisms *because they are made up of people.* When we speak of 'organisational stress' we mean the over-spill of stress from the 'people' part of the three resources. I said that stress can develop because of an undue emphasis placed on any one of the resources. It can also occur because of inadequate attention to one or more of the three, resulting in disharmony and imbalance.

The impression should not be given that stress is undesir-able; we all need a certain amount of stress, or tension, to keep us going but all of us have what is called 'the stress threshold'. Stress which rises above this threshold will cause us to crack; just like the overheated engine. A useful illustra-tion of stress is to think of the person as a tank. If water is poured into a tank it will eventually start to spill over. Some tanks are small; some are large. The tank did not say to its maker, "Make me large so that I can hold more", it just is. So with people, some can tolerate less stress than others before they show signs of cracking. It does not mean that one person is weaker than the other—it just means that he has a lower threshold—in other words a smaller stress tank. *But we all have a point at which we will crack*—when the water will start to overflow.

One way in which organisations contribute towards a build-up of stress within individuals is by a constant pushing

11

in of orders, requests, demands, unrealistic expectations, without providing the means for outlet, except to spill over the top. A department, an office, a person, can only take in so much before indigestion sets in; indigestion is one form of stress. If there is a continual input from 'up top' (maybe for yet another impossible dead-line), frustration, anxiety, fear, conflict and tension build up and push the stress nearer the threshold. It only requires one last proverbial straw to create an eruption.

People crack in different ways. Not all will 'blow', like the overheated engine; not all take industrial action; not all go sick or absent themselves or spend time in the toilet. Some turn the frustration and anger inwards, towards themselves, which results in an inability to cope with everyday situations. The frustration may be expressed outwards, not against the people most directly concerned (those at work), but against those who are not involved—family, neighbours, friends. The deterioration in relationships which is likely to result from this displaced frustration, must in turn influence performance at work. The end result of undue stress is a decrease in personal and organisational efficiency.

Something organisations *can* do to ensure that stress does not build up to danger levels is to provide safety valves— outlets to take some of the heat out of a potentially explosive situation. Established channels of communication upwards will assist, but these channels must be used effectively. It is not a bit of good encouraging people to communicate upwards about how they feel if those at the top listen and do nothing and the situation remains as it was. If nothing can be done to change the system, because of other pressures and demands (not immediately appreciated by those lower down), the situation could be eased by putting before them the pros and cons. If nothing is done, one more bit of stress is added.

TO CARE OR NOT TO CARE?

A notice prominently displayed in a machine shop reads "A little oil, a little care, saves lots of worry and lots of wear." Machines of all kinds need oil, and machinists know that the most effective use they can make of the oilcan is little and often. Inexperienced people often let the machine run bone-dry and hope to remedy the situation by an over-zealous use of the oilcan; such injudicious use of the oil has a tendency to produce the opposite effect—to slow up the machines, again producing stress.

Organisations are no different! I believe that just as the machinist needs to 'care' for his machine, in order to get the most out of it, so managers need to care for their part of the organisation. This caring is not a sentimental, slushy attitude but is practical and, if you like, motivated by profit, or efficiency. People who are concerned with machines, say typewriters, clean them, have them serviced regularly and generally maintain them in tip-top condition. People who are concerned with money are meticulous in accounting for it and how it is safeguarded. Those who are concerned with materials, again, are careful to ensure that each separate item is accounted for and stored in strict accordance with pre-scribed schedules. But what about the 'people' part of the organisation? Do we care for them as much as we do for machines, money and materials? People are not expendable, cannot be written off against income tax or annual deprecia-tion and yet very often they receive less attention, less tender loving care, than the inanimate objects which clutter many offices.

We can attach valves to boilers and temperature gauges to engines to ensure that the machine is not irreparably damaged. We become very skilled at reading warning signs of impending disaster in our various machines but oh, what an indictment, that so very often we cannot read very definite warning signs of intolerable stress in our fellow human beings!

If oil is essential to keep machinery running smoothly, I would suggest that what is needed to keep the wheels of the organisation moving freely is the oil of caring. When people have a genuine caring attitude, it shows. It shows, not in always telling how much we care, not in always living in each other's pockets, not in getting 'matey' and in the use of Christian names. It shows in a genuine concern for the worth of each person as a human being, made exactly as we are. Caring shows in an acceptance of the differences and limita-tions of others with a humility based on the sure knowledge that other people have to accept *our* limitations and defects and that we are more similar to them than we are different. Caring shows in our being able to accept those of different intelligence, social class and occupational status. It may be easier to accept those of what we consider a 'lower' social class, intelligence or occupational status than those above us!

I do not mean that we have to accept unacceptable behaviour or standards with which we are at variance; that would be allowing the individual to shed responsibility. There are some people who are only too willing to blame society, the law, their parents and a whole host of others for the fact that they, in some way, conflict with others. There are also others (who in their opinion 'care' for them), who foster this attitude by colluding with them; that is neither caring nor acceptance; it is shortsightedness. No doubt they all have good intentions but good intentions often spring from ulterior motives.

The acceptance I mean is akin to the Biblical 'To love the sinner but not the sin'. If we can get behind the action, or the deed which is unacceptable, and try to understand the motives, feelings and attitudes, we shall have travelled some way along the road from rejection to acceptance, from ignorance to understanding.

CARING COMMUNICATION

A caring attitude is the oil which keeps the whole organisation running smoothly but there is one last factor to be considered—communication. If caring is the oil, communication is the channel of influence by which caring is conveyed from person and from one part of the organisation to the other.

Thoughts, feelings, ideas and concepts are conveyed through words, although of course they may also be conveyed through non-verbal language. To be effective, what is said must be interpreted and accepted by the recipient. It is sometimes thought that business communication is straightforward—concerned only with facts, and that emotions are excluded. This is not true. Feelings will show through in the words we use, however much we try to disguise them.

So very often effective communication is marred by a hastily written letter, written, perhaps in a temper (not necessarily aimed at the person to whom the letter is addressed) or in a mood of frustration. Something in the tone will cause the recipient to bristle; as a result, it is likely that the whole communication will be rejected.

What are your feelings when you read this?

> Dear . . .
> The next meeting of the executive is on . . . at . . . will you please make arrangements to attend.
> Yours etc. . . .

The very obvious peremptory tone caused *me* to bristle. I tackled the writer (a senior Personnel Manager) who passed the blame to his secretary. If this secretary had picked up from her boss any caring, it would surely have showed through in the way she wrote his letters.

Attitudes are clearly displayed in what we say and write, and of course there are those people who maintain that as managers their task is to get the job done and if people are so sensitive that they jib at what is said or written that is not their affair. To me that is saying that they do not care. Is it also saying, "I don't care whom I trample on in my way to where I am going?"

Effective communication depends upon sending a clear signal and that signal being received by a 'receiver'—like radio signals. Words are very often totally inadequate to express what we want to say and frequently what is said is distorted by emotion. I am quite certain that the secretary above did not mean to 'order' the executive members to attend, but that is how it actually came over (at least to me). Choice of words, in the first place, is important—do they convey explicitly the thought, idea, concept we wish to put across? When this is established, the next consideration is—how is what we have said likely to be received? In dealing with people we need to develop the faculty of empathy and to place ourselves in the place of the other person who will receive our communication. A careful re-reading of the letter, listening to the emotional overtones, will teach us a great deal about our own feelings and how we come over to other people.

Effective communication is dependent not only on the accuracy of the signal being sent but on the accuracy of the receiver; both need to be on the same wavelength. If the tuning mechanism of either is out of true, distortion will result. Emotions are like the tuning mechanism, the function of which is to protect us so that we hear only what is 'safe' for us to hear; what is not 'safe' will be distorted or cut out completely.

From an early age we learn what is safe and unsafe to say to other people. Very often we learn the difference through some painful lesson but with the passage of time the actual experience recedes from our memory, leaving behind an emotional after-image (like we get when we look at a bright light then close our eyes). It is these emotional after-images which cause us so many problems when we communicate; we transmit and receive through mists laden with past emotions.

The words we want to use trigger off many of these memories, our emotional tuner immediately moves off wavelength, perhaps only fractionally, and the result is distortion of what we actually want to say (or hear). In written communication it is more possible to monitor what we say than it is in face-to-face conversation because in speech we do not have quite the same opportunity to consider what we have said and modify it.

The person to whom we are talking, or writing, has his own in-built emotional tuner which monitors what *he* receives in order to safeguard *his* emotional status quo. His life experiences will be different from ours, so his emotional tuner will be selecting different things to accept, reject or modify.

From this illustration it will be evident that any two-way communication, written or verbal, is liable to a great deal of misinterpretation and confusion. The person who cares for other people will be careful that the words he uses will not lead to rejection of what he is trying to say. An awareness of having said the wrong thing should lead to an analysis of

16

why, how it can be rectified and how a similar rejection could be avoided in the future.

THE PRE–COUNSELLING RELATIONSHIP

Counselling is a relationship in which thoughts and feelings can be explored in an atmosphere of trust. Much of what takes place during counselling depends on verbal exchange (mainly but not exclusively). If words can be distorted by emotions, it follows that the more the counsellor has insight into his own emotional mechanisms, the less distortion will occur. Insight into his own emotions will provide him with greater understanding of the emotional mechanisms of people being counselled.

Counselling a member of staff is more likely to arise spontaneously if the relationship is established and fostered over a considerable time. If the manager demonstrates his willingness and ability to move out towards his staff on a human level and they feel confident that they can trust him, they will feel more able to approach him with problems.

The manager who does not establish this pre-counselling relationship will have the balances weighted against him when *he* attempts to counsel, even if he recognises the need—for instance because of some performance problem.

Unless this pre-counselling relationship is firmly establish-ed, counselling, if attempted, is likely to be formal and stilted with both parties very much on guard. You cannot expect two people who have had little or no emotional contact suddenly to start dealing constructively with emotional issues, especially if it is the manager who has initiated the session.

The situation is different when a person with a problem approaches someone for help; he has already gone through a selection process in his mind as to whom he should approach. Very often the person chosen is completely unknown, at a personal level, and of course this does have advantages in that there is little chance of pre-judgment or bias. It is more likely that personal problems are dealt with in this way—by the professional counsellor or someone having a definite counselling remit as part of their job. But it is also true that many people are able to talk through their difficulties with people who, although not professionals, are skilled in problem-solving. The professional counsellor may be at an advantage in that he does not know anything about the person and, as I have already indicated, this may obviate bias. The fact that he does not know anything may also present difficulties. He has to rely on what the client says, and we are all very prone to put our own case strongly and to reveal only those points we wish to make known. Managers have a great deal of first-hand knowledge of the staff members they are counselling and they would be less likely to have the wool pulled over their eyes. Someone not involved—the professional counsellor, for instance—could be at a disadvantage. This does not in any sense demean the ability of the professional to perceive inconsistencies.

AUTHORITY AND COUNSELLING

One final aspect must be dealt with before this chapter is drawn to a conclusion: authority, and its related aspect of power. The dividing line between authority and power is finely drawn, but broadly speaking, authority, if it is to be effective, must be accepted by those who are subject to its control. Power denotes the influence one person has over another or others to make them do something against their will.

Many people have been subjected to misuse of authority and power at the hands of power-mad N.C.O.s in the Services. Authority is handed down from the Sovereign and very often the N.C.O. has to make people do things against their will, even in the course of what is within the bounds of normal; e.g. drill. The majority of the time he is acting in strict accordance with sanctioned power. The N.C.O. who, on the other hand, makes slaves or puppets of his recruits is abusing the power of his authority. Abuse of power springs from the same source as dominance.

Managers have a certain authority by virtue of their position in the organisation. The majority of staff never

18

question this authority—in other words they sanction it. With this authority goes a certain degree of power—if power is influencing people to do things against their will—in that he can insist that certain procedures are adopted and carried out.

The student nurse who does not want to arrive on duty on time, if challenged by the Ward Sister and forced to comply, is being subjected to her authority and the power which is invested in her. If that same Sister were to exercise her power to compel her staff to work every day an hour longer than necessary she would be abusing her authority and power.

If the authority of the manager is accepted and seen to be just, if his power is wielded with care and is seen to be fair and he has not misused his position of authority, and if, when discipline was necessary, it was meted out with justice, then counselling should present no difficulty.

Managers, because they exercise authority, are in a similar position to Probation Officers who are placed in authority over their clients. Many other social workers are also in positions of authority; those working with children on Court Orders, those working with the mentally ill. All these people have to come to terms with the fact that their clients are placed under their authority and at the same time they have to establish a helping relationship.

The finest example of the dual role of authority and helper is the parental relationship. Parents have a great deal of authority, power and influence over their children. Some abuse that authority and produce rebels; the majority genuinely strive to exercise a control which is aimed at producing a generation of people who will carry civilisation forward. The majority of parents know that for the young child to develop his own personality he must be permitted to grow in his own way, within an atmosphere of security. Security is more than a warm loving embrace; it also means knowing exactly where his boundaries are. As he develops, these boundaries are extended by a judicious pushing on his part and a releasing on the part of his parents. The child needs to develop in an atmosphere of consistent authority and control which is exercised by parents who themselves have accepted authority and who are not afraid to set boundaries. A child reared without boundaries will forever seek to escape from the wilderness of the wide world into which he has prematurely strayed. The manager who feels unable to counsel because of his position, should take stock of his own attitudes towards authority.

SUMMARY

This chapter introduces some of the basic premises about the relationships between staff, and how these relationships may be influenced. It may be difficult to strike a balance between concern for a member of staff and over-concern which would amount to prying. If concern springs from a genuine caring there will be less danger of what the manager does being interpreted as interference.

Counselling is one way in which all members of staff can improve their over-all relationships with people; the more we participate in counselling the more our own emotions, attitudes, opinions, beliefs and motives are brought under the microscope. The result of this examination should lead to a far greater understanding of 'self' in relation to others.

Managers must maintain a balance between the three resources of money, materials and people. If these three wheels are not kept turning smoothly in all areas, the organisation will suffer from stress. Stress can also build up in people from internal or personal causes, but may also arise from external causes imposed upon them by the organisation. Stress can never be totally eradicated; stress which is excessive and unwarranted should be avoided. A caring attitude between staff, particularly by those in authority, is one way in which personal and organisational stress can be diminished.

Effective communication, which is one way of reducing stress, demands as much thought and care as any other aspect of management. Both communicator and recipient have built-in emotional mechanisms which carefully monitor what is said (or written) and heard (or read); the function of this mechanism is to decide what is 'safe' to be received; distortion frequently results.

Counselling is concerned with establishing a caring relationship in which both counsellor and counsellee seek ways in which they can communicate effectively about a problem. Effective counselling by the manager of his own staff depends upon establishing a pre-counselling relationship of caring and trust. The manager's use or abuse of authority and power will influence his relationship with his staff and so make or mar his chances of being an effective staff counsellor.

CHAPTER 2

What Counselling Is and Is Not

WORDS

In the previous chapter we looked at some of the fundamental attitudes essential for effective counselling whether the problem is personal or related to work. This chapter will examine some of the concepts not already dealt with, under the two broad headings—what counselling is and is not. At times there may be overlap between what is said in this chapter and what is said elsewhere in the book. This is inevitable; it is difficult and not wholly desirable to deal with all subjects in water-tight compartments.

When any subject is considered it is often useful to examine it under these two headings—"is" and "is not". Very few things are as black or as white as I appear to suggest, and as we look at some of the points we shall see that the "is" and "is not" frequently become blurred.

I use this approach in teaching counselling by asking groups to identify what they think counselling is and is not; then the various points are explored. Usually it is easier to define the "is" than the "is not". For this reason I will examine these points in pairs of opposites. It is possible that these couples are not precisely opposites in dictionary definitions; some may be different derivations of the same root. It may also be that some of the words would be better replaced by others. Taking these reservations into account, please bear with me; try not to quarrel with the words but examine the underlying meaning and the concept or theme which I am trying to express.

There is a danger when writing, as I said in the previous chapter, that what I want to say will be distorted by my own emotions. If you find yourself at variance with anything I say, pay particular attention to that, for it may be that your own internal mechanism is rejecting something on emotional grounds. It could also be that I have not explained the point clearly enough, or that the words are unfamiliar.

Another difficulty in communication is the words themselves. I said that words convey feelings, but any one word is capable of conveying various feelings according to the meaning attached to it by the communicator and recipient. We must accept that not everyone uses the same vocabulary; this is largely a matter of education, social class, interest, occupation and culture. People of the same background are more likely to understand the words used by one another than are those of different backgrounds, merely because of the difference in meanings attached to words.

Another aspect of the language used is jargon. It may be accepted as quite normal to use certain words to describe specific objects, concepts or procedures. Usually this presents no problem provided all the people concerned have learned the language. People of one occupation (and jargon is invariably linked with occupations) may have difficulty understanding the jargon of another. Student nurses often feel over-whelmed when they start training. Quite apart from all the procedures they have to learn, there is a whole new language; and all those abbreviations! Abbreviations are but one facet of what I have been referring to as 'jargon'. If nurses feel bewildered it would be salutory to reflect on how the patient may feel when surrounded on all sides by people using a strange language which excludes him.

Counselling is based on ideas, concepts and principles, which have their origins in other disciplines—philosophy, ethics, psychology, social work, psychiatry and religion. A consequence of this is that some of the jargon from these disciplines has been integrated into the language of counselling. One of the difficulties of taking over language from another discipline is that different meanings become attached to the words with a consequent confusion. I hope that this book is relatively free from unfamiliar terms; or if words and terms are unfamiliar that the context in which they are used will make clear their meaning.

Britain, like many other countries, is rapidly becoming multi-racial, and one of the results is that clear-cut cultural distinctions are becoming blurred. The bringing together of different nationalities inevitably creates problems, not only of prejudice, resentment and fear but of bewilderment and frustration in both incomer and host. Cultural differences are often difficult to understand and the understanding is not simplified by the language differences. We need not take examples from different nationalities: within our own nation we have many examples of cultural differences as extreme as between us and some immigrants. I remember causing a shop assistant much amusement and myself much embarrassment when, a few days after arriving in England from Scotland, I asked for ". . . one of those cookies in the window." Only after using sign language did I get my 'bun'. Some years later, when working for a Yorkshire farmer in the South, and unable to tie a knot in the baling twine because of the extreme cold, my pride was injured when he said "He lad, are your hands soft?" My looks must have conveyed my feelings of hurt manhood, "Don't take on lad," he said with a grin, "that's Yorkshire, it means your hands are useless wi' the cold." A very early lesson in cultural confusion!

These introductory remarks will, I hope, have paved the way for the main part of this chapter. I hope you have already started to relate what you have read to your own life's experience and that you will be able to draw something from within yourself to illustrate the different points being considered. I cannot emphasise too strongly how essential it is, when counselling, to ensure that you understand precisely what the other person is trying to say. Just as important as it is that he understands what you are trying to say.

This two-way understanding, which is the sharing basis of any productive relationship, rests mainly with you. You are the counsellor, the one who is standing outside the problem, who is objective, and you will have to show him, teach him, how to put into words what he feels and to use the words which will best convey these feelings. You can do this by constantly establishing that what you have said has been understood.

Many people, when asked if they understand, are reluctant to admit that they do not. It could be a reflection of their intellectual grasp but they could feel embarrassed for you, that you have not put over your ideas very clearly. A useful approach is to say something like, "Does that sound complicated (or difficult or garbled) to you?" "Tell me what you think I've been trying to say, then I can see if I've put it clearly."

You could say "Does that sound complicated. . . . Tell me what you think I'm trying to say so that I can see if you have understood it clearly." What difference strikes you about these two approaches?

The implication of the second approach is that if there is difficulty in understanding, it lies with him, with his grasp and not the way in which you expressed yourself. Rather like a lecturer with a group of students; if they do not understand, it must be them, or so many lecturers think, but in reality it is probably the way he is putting the subject across.

The second approach could lead the other person to feel annoyed and slightly inferior. If this sounds like taking the blame—it is; but that is seldom a bad thing.

Just as you have to ensure that what you have said is understood accurately, you must make certain that you understand what he says. Again, try not to give the impression that he is not expressing himself adequately. Asking for clarification is one way of helping him to express himself more clearly. After all, this may be one of the problems he has—that he finds it difficult to express himself adequately, especially when dealing with emotional topics. Let your time together be a positive learning experience which will enrich his experience and your counselling skills.

We shall now consider twelve paired concepts, first under the heading "is", then "is not". Before you continue, will you please refer back to paragraph 3 of this chapter.

COUNSELLING IS — RELATIONSHIP
IT IS NOT — PSYCHOANALYSIS

What is a relationship? It is something between (in this context) two people which is founded upon what brings them together and keeps them together. This is a positive relationship. A negative relationship is what comes between two people, keeping them apart. I'm sure we can all think of people we know, possibly relationships in which we have been involved, where these two opposites could apply— negative or positive.

Jean and Mary were both Staff Nurses on the same ward. Both were well-adjusted girls, married with children, and were both respected by all members of the staff. They had 'good' relationships with everyone—everyone, that is, except each other. Something had come between them very early in their time on the ward and their contacts were marred by this negative barrier which kept them from establishing a positive relationship.

Their attitude towards each other affected their work in as much that when one of them made a suggestion for improving some procedure on the ward, the other would veto it. Minor defects were blown up into huge issues, and as a consequence this negative field of influence began to pervade the whole ward.

The Sister realised that it would be difficult, if not impossible, to achieve complete reconciliation and she would have to be satisfied with a compromise. She wanted to introduce a new system of patient-care and needed cooperation from both of them. She spoke to them individually about her ideas, getting their opinions and thoughts. She then brought them together in a discussion about the methods and principles and how the whole project could be implemented and their respective responsibilities. When she did bring them together she was careful to ensure that she allowed both of them equal opportunity to express their opinions and ideas, and when it looked as if they were starting to get into a negative dialogue she would interject with another new slant, still on the subject of the project; never allowing the discussion to degenerate into a discussion of personal issues. This common interest brought them closer together on neutral (professional) ground. Their relationship began to be less negative as they started to establish common ground.

Positive relationships are established on common ground; such as common attitudes, interests, occupations, religion, hobby or pastimes. Couples build their marriages on little plots of common ground which gradually enlarge as they get to know more about each other. Couples who feel that this common ground has been eroded have little to help them to stay together. They frequently divorce, having little left in common.

Give and Take

The small plot, upon which any relationship is established, develops out of what both give to each other. This 'give' and 'take' is vital and the process must be continuous. A relationship is like a reservoir of water; one person pours some water in, the other is free to take from the reservoir to meet his need. He, in turn, will give, so that the other may take. When the giving exceeds the taking, the relationship will expand. When one person stops giving or when both restrict their giving but continue to take, the reservoir will eventually shrink and run dry.

Counselling is a relationship, and the same principle of give and take applies. If counselling is to be effective it must be productive, and if the illustration of the reservoir is continued, both counsellor and client will put something of themselves into that reservoir.

I indicated previously that one of the ways in which you can help someone being counselled is to show him how to explore his emotions, but in so doing you will both be required to give, simply because emotions are in focus.

Above all, he wants to see you as a real person with real feelings. It may be that you have weaknesses and defects; that is reality and the counsellee is able to use this reality to test his own feelings and reactions.

A young nurse came to her tutor to discuss whether she should discontinue training as a student. As they explored the question it emerged quite clearly that she could not cope with certain groups of patients. With the young and old she had no problem, but with both men and women in early middle-age she experienced great anxiety. The tutor asked a simple question, "Why do you think that is?" After a few minutes' pause the student said, through eyes filled with tears, "I think of my mum and dad." She felt very guilty about not being able to continue, and the tutor felt disappointment that a promising student should discontinue but she realised that the student had made up her mind. She wanted to give something positive to her and apart from saying that possibly with a little more experience of life she might be able to continue training, she told her that even with all her years of experience, she found working with deformity very traumatic and anxiety-provoking. The student looked relieved as she said "Oh, I'm glad you said that, I thought I was the only one who ever felt like this and that I would never be able to make a good nurse."

This illustration points to how a little giving goes a long way. This was positive and something constructive in that relationship. It meant that the student could take from it what she needed—some comfort that she was not alone in having these feelings.

Questions

Why was the age of the patients relevant in this case?
Could the tutor have helped the student more than she did?
What would you have done?

Secure Foundations

Any counsellor can only contribute positively to the counselling relationship from a secure foundation. In any area in which he does not feel secure, he will be liable to erect

29

barriers, thus breaking contact at the point where the client most needs help. None of us is absolutely secure in all areas of our emotions; we all have 'grey' areas where emotional development has lagged behind, where the emotions are primitive and unpredictable, where we have not achieved insight.

The client and counsellor make and maintain emotional contact in areas where insight has been achieved; where insight is lacking or incomplete, emotional contact is super-ficial and generally unproductive. It is possible that a particular client, because of the nature of his problem, may only make contact with those areas within the counsellor which are known—where insight has been achieved. It is also possible that another client, by the nature of *his* specific problem and the accompanying cluster of emotions, will encounter an area not hitherto touched upon—a grey area where insight is incomplete.

The manager who embarks upon counselling, places himself in the position of a constant appraisal of his inner-self through the emotional encounters with various clients. If it so happens that someone you are counselling touches an emotional trigger within you, two things may happen. You can immediately bring the shutter down or you can examine how you feel there and then.

If you take the first course of action, you are in danger of breaking contact. You can avoid this happening, however, by saying something like, "I don't think I can help you to ex-plore that at this stage; we have touched some emotion in me and I don't know how to deal with it." This is not easy and generally can only be done when you feel secure enough within your counselling role.

Mr Stevens, a Senior Nursing Officer, was talking to one of his Ward Sisters who had been creating problems in the hospital. After about half an hour he felt himself becoming angry although he was trying his best to conceal it. He said, "Sister, I wonder if we could call it a day? I find I am be-coming irritated and can't think why. If we carry on I may start making you angry too and that wouldn't help."

30

He was puzzled by his reaction (he prided himself on being able to keep his temper under most circumstances) and talked it over with one of his colleagues who was more experienced in counselling. They explored the case and as they did so it gradually dawned on Mr Stevens that one of his grey areas had been touched on. Sister Jones was known to be a highly manipulative person who created divisions among her staff. Mr Stevens knew this and couldn't see why he should have been so angry. His friend explored with him a little more and said "Does Sister remind you of anyone?" Quite suddenly Mr Stevens had a mental picture of his wife. He told his friend, and as they examined this Mr Stevens realised that Sister Jones' behaviour closely matched that of his wife's in many ways—which was always a bone of contention in their marriage. There had been many heated arguments between them, especially when he refused to be manipulated. When Mr Stevens next met Sister he was able to adopt a more objective approach.

Mr Stevens did not bring the shutter down and was able to deal constructively with an area which could have been a constant source of annoyance between himself and Sister Jones.

Some trigger spots are just too painful to allow anyone to touch; another reason why the shutter is drawn down. But, and I repeat what I said earlier, if the person being counselled is to be helped *at his point of need*, you yourself must achieve insight into that problem area *within you* so that you can make positive emotional contact.

The section you have just read could have been included under a later discussion of Exploration (page 49) but it seemed right to include it here; this emphasises how difficult it is to keep subjects in water-tight compartments.

Trust in Counselling

No relationship could exist without trust and we saw how mistrust was one of the barriers which created a negative relationship between the two Staff Nurses (page 27). There are four aspects of trust I wish to consider.

Firstly both manager and counsellee must trust each other. The counsellee must trust the integrity and justice of the manager as a person. This links up with what has been said earlier about the pre-counselling relationship. If he knows the manager to be less than honest in his dealings with people he is unlikely to feel confidence in him during counselling.

The second point is that the counsellee must trust the manager's ability to counsel effectively. He may know that the manager is relatively unskilled in counselling, and yet still trust him to counsel effectively because he trusts him as a person.

The third point is that the counsellee will trust what the manager says and does as being right and proper and in his best interests. For instance it may be necessary to explore the family relationships in order to point to similarities between them and relationships at work. If, however, the manager is really a voyeur and seeks details about the counsellee's personal life which may have no bearing on the case, the counsellee will probably feel his trust has been betrayed.

Confidentiality and Trust

The fourth point is that of confidentiality. Elsewhere I draw a distinction between what is 'confidential' and what is 'secret'.* Sometimes it may be essential to discuss a particular case with another person—as Mr Stevens did. It is not always easy deciding between what is confidential and what is secret. The knowledge that you will not gossip about him must give your staff member a degree of confidence and trust in you, and must in some way determine the amount or degree of exploration he will permit.

In the course of counselling, the client may divulge certain aspects of his personal life which normally he would keep secret. Sometimes, however, details which he would classify 'secret' must be brought into the open, albeit to a limited circle of people.

The manager should be careful of allowing the counsellee to secure an unconditional guarantee of confidentiality before learning all the facts. Confidentiality needs to be spelled out

* *A Guide to Counselling*, William Stewart, p.7.

quite clearly to the counsellee for you, as manager, have your areas of responsibility, particularly to the organisation which employs you. It may be helpful for you and the client to establish just what both of you mean by confidentiality. Everyone will have a different idea, and if the boundaries are established at the outset, the counsellee will feel more freedom to move than if it had not been dealt with at all.

Most people will respond positively to this approach, feeling that you are helping them to set their own objectives. It is for them then to decide precisely what they will discuss or what they will keep hidden.

Ease the cork out

Some people have the idea that all must be revealed before they can be helped. With this (mistaken, in my opinion) idea in mind, they pour out their hearts and hope that by so doing they will feel better. The watchful counsellor is alert to this and will keep a gentle foot on the client's emotional brake. Too much revealed too soon may create an emotional vacuum, the result of which could be despair coupled with resentment towards the counsellor. When put into words it would be something like "How can I face him *now,* when he knows all that about me?" In a sense the counsellor has become a scapegoat. No one, unless he is a masochist, would enjoy such an experience and I'm quite certain you can see what havoc this could create in the relationship between a manager and his staff.

It may not be easy to stop the emotional flow once it has started. It is like taking the cork out of the bottle; there is no knowing what may emerge. But the counsellor can avoid too rapid an emptying, by allowing the counsellee to ease the cork out himself. But do remember the 'brake'!

Trusting the Client

I said that for a relationship to be productive there must be give and take on both sides and this involves trust. We have looked at how essential it is for the client to trust the counsellor, but it is equally important that the counsellor is able to trust the client. If he is unsure that *his* confidence will be respected he will be hesitant to give of that 'something' which may make all the difference in the relationship. That is another reason why the whole area of confidentiality and trust needs to be explored.

For instance, when counselling I always get past this point early on. I tell the client that he does not have to make a secret of the fact that he is involved in counselling and if he wishes to explain why, that is his privilege. What he should not do is to talk about the details of what takes place. One reason for this is that he may become confused if a number of people offer their solutions and possibly add to the conflict. There is also the danger that some unscrupulous person will try to capitalise on the information gleaned. In any case, to talk about the details to anyone else is not keeping to the contract of confidentiality.

Sometimes, especially when a married person is being counselled, the spouse (or in some cases the girl friend, or boy friend) can become quite jealous of the relationship between counsellor and client. Mixed with this feeling, there may be guilt, which if expressed would be something like, "Why is it that he can do so much with . . . when I can't?; What is he telling him about me?"; "Is he going to take him away from me?" (This is likely to apply even more if the counsellor and client are of opposite sexes.)

A similar type of feeling could be expressed by members of staff who know that one of their colleagues is receiving counselling fairly frequently, from you. If counselling has to be carried out over a number of sessions (and this is possible and often necessary), it may appear to the others that so-and-so is getting more of your time than they are; will this counselling lead to a special relationship between you? and so on. These feelings may apply even more if one of the other staff has a particularly close relationship with the person being counselled.

All this may sound a bit juvenile but there is a certain degree of truth in the theory that relationships in any department are closely modelled on the family, with the manager as 'father', and if he pays too much attention to one, how do the others feel? If they do feel neglected, think how they may try and compensate for these feelings; how may they react towards 'father-manager'?; how may they react towards the counsellee? how may behaviour between themselves alter? Think around these questions and then think how you could possibly avoid such a situation developing within your own department.

The second premise of this section is that counselling is not psychoanalysis. I said that counselling has developed out of many disciplines and we owe a great deal to the psycho-analysts in the understanding they have given us of the unconscious and how it influences behaviour.

What is Psychoanalysis?

The principal difference between psychoanalysis and counsel-ling is that psychoanalysis deals more, but not exclusively, with the unconscious and the past, while counselling deals more, but not exclusively, with the conscious and the present—the here-and-now and the very recent past.

I say 'more, but not exclusively' and this needs to be qualified. The counsellor cannot ignore the unconscious. The past and the present are bound together with cords that cannot be broken and it is inevitable that things from the past will pop through into the conscious present. When this happens the client will usually be aware of it. This flash of insight carries with it a certain excitement and anticipation of pleasure. It is like walking into a house which you have not visited for many years—it is vaguely familiar. Merely a smell, a picture, a sound, will bring back floods of forgotten memories and emotions.

When this happens, both counsellor and client can be caught up in excitement as they feel that here at last is 'the' clue to the whole problem. In an attempt to explore this avenue they flog this little bit of insight to death by a con-stant probing and trying to get more out of it. But sadly it is realised that what had the promise of a profitable exploration has turned into a barren cul-de-sac instead of a broad high-way to liberty.

Try not to do this. Be like the artist, who, beholding a beautiful sunset, savours all its qualities, but passes on, knowing that even his best attempt to faithfully capture it will be but a travesty. Leave the client with his insight; let him work on it in his own way, in his own time and do not rob him of the thrill of achieving self-insight by your unnecessary probing into the recesses of his past.

Having said this, however, I do not want to give the impression either that exploration of the past has no place in counselling or that probing is inappropriate and unnecessary. I have said that the past and the present are inseparable and if this is so then the one cannot be examined without some part of the other emerging; it is all a matter of degree and emphasis.

The past will show its influence quite clearly; and if dealt with when appropriate, will yield fruit. Too much emphasis on the past can detract from the present thus allowing the client to escape into a world of phantasy in which he, and you, could spend endless hours searching for ". . . such stuffs as dreams are made on," at the expense of keeping in touch with reality.

Probing (whether into the past or the present) needs to be executed with the delicate skill of the nurse probing a tender wound. In fact it is more successful if the client himself does the probing while you direct and guide his hand. However sensitive you may be, only he can really tell when a particular tender area has been touched. If he is being helped to do his own probing, he will know when to stop and take a rest. The client who thus learns to do his own exploring will have acquired a valuable tool which he can put to good use in the future.

COUNSELLING IS – LISTENING
IT IS NOT – INTERROGATION

These two words have been brought together for a definite reason. Could I just ask you what you understand by interrogation? Don't look it up in a dictionary, just write your thoughts down and keep your notes to hand until you have read through this section.

In Chapter 1 I pointed out some of the reasons why listening may be difficult. Listening and hearing are two different aspects of the same activity; listening is an attempt to hear and, as we have already discovered, what we hear can be very different from what the speaker thinks we will hear.

Listening presupposes there is one person to speak and another to hear, and someone has said that the world is made up of two types of people—those who talk and those who listen. Be that as it may, effective counselling is founded on effective listening; but what is effective listening? It is hearing what the other person is saying and this means hearing what he is trying to say as well as what he is actually saying. Many people listen but few hear. A person who is partially deaf may strive hard to listen but may miss a great deal of what is really said. That person cannot be accused of not listening, but it is frustrating for him and others when what they say is not heard.

Many people in normal conversation do not hear what is being said because their attention has been diverted into a different channel, either because of the subject matter or from some other stimulus. It can also happen that people do not hear because of some strong emotion. Another possible reason is that they have ceased to listen because *they* want to start speaking. Some people find it difficult to listen for very long to someone else speaking.

Counselling involves both client and counsellor in listening and talking. If the aim of counselling is to encourage someone to talk about his problem, in all its aspects, then it is obvious that the counsellor must be a listener. I have said that effective listening in counselling is an active process of hearing what the client says and what he is trying to say: it certainly is not a passive soaking up of everything the client says without making responses. It is a careful monitoring of the words to try and understand their contextual meaning and the underlying emotions.

The counsellor, like anyone else, may be subject to wandering attention, and this could apply particularly in the work environment. Things which may distract and cause your attention to wander, and so cause the listening ear to become deaf, may arise from within or without. You may have a mountain of work on your desk, some imminent deadline to be met; you may have a meeting to attend and you have not done your homework for it; you may hear 'noises off'—a machine making a strange noise which could indicate disaster, the noise of a patient in distress, and although you know he is being attended to you are still anxious; you may be tired, hungry, or feel jaded. All these things (and more) may cause your attention to wander and so interfere with effective listening. We must all acquire the facility of dealing with one thing at a time and excluding all others, though this may not be easy; the manager is constantly being forced into situations where he must cope with a multiplicity of tasks simultaneously. The person you are counselling must feel at that moment, and throughout the session, that your time is for him alone; that he has your undivided attention.

Question

We all have various concerns which would cause our attention to wander. These may be grouped under 'personal', 'inter-personal' and 'work'. Obviously everyone is different and even though two people do the same work they are likely to respond differently to various stimuli. Taking these three headings, jot down some of the points you know would be likely to distract *you* and cause your attention to wander. I, for instance, am easily distracted by a child crying in a distressed manner; I find it difficult to ignore the ring of the telephone. How about you?

Asking Questions

I have indicated that listening is an active process involving hearing the unspoken word as well as the spoken. But counselling is not simply listening; it involves asking questions. Question-asking is as much a skill as listening. It is in this area that we consider the statement that counselling is not in-terrogation.

Interrogation

At the beginning of this section I invited you to write down your thoughts on interrogation. You may now like to re-read them before you read my thoughts. Interrogation certainly involves asking questions, but it is how and why they are asked which constitutes the difference between that and

counselling. Questions asked under pressure or duress con-
stitute interrogation. A suspect, cross-examined by the police,
is interrogated. We think of an interrogation scene with its
bombardment of questions calculated to break down the
resistance of the captive.

This is extreme, I know, and it is doubtful if anyone would
imagine counselling to be conducted on these lines. But, and
this is the point, *how* questions are asked *can make the
counsellee feel he is undergoing interrogation.* How many
times have you listened to a scene in a court-room where the
prosecuting counsel, with his clever questions, has tied the
defendant in knots or has him running round in verbal
circles? One of the techniques used in cross-examination is
to ask a series of questions which are so linked that it is
almost impossible to tell the truth, even if the defendant
could unravel the questions from each other. The result is
a build-up of bewilderment and fear which it is calculated
will lower his defences, and a confession of guilt will then
be extracted.

The aim of counselling is certainly not to extract con-
fessions, admissions of failure, or disclosures of secrets
against the person's will. What then is the purpose of asking
questions and how should they be asked so as not to induce
or heighten anxiety, fear or anger?

Get him talking

The first thing to remember is that it is essential to get the
person to talk. To keep him talking about the problem you
may need to ask questions pertinent to what he is telling you.
Questions should, as it were, 'keep the pot boiling' and you
can do this quite effectively by such questions as "Tell me
what you did then," "How many jobs did you say you have
been in?", "You said a few minutes ago that you didn't like
working with women, tell me a bit more about that."

You may have a certain number of questions you need
answered, and it is surprising how you can link these to
something which has already been brought out. Do try and
make every question relate to the whole; make sure he
understands why you have asked a particular question and
its relevance.

Don't ask questions to which a 'yes' or 'no' answer is possible unless the answer required is factual. "Do you drive a car?" is a question which calls for a 'yes' or 'no' although even in this, the answer may be significant. If he were to answer "No, not now", what would your next question be? If he did answer in this way instead of a straightforward 'No', what would you read between the lines? This little additional bit of information may lead you on to a discussion of some importance. If you wanted to enquire about his relationships with other staff, "Tell me how you get on with the other staff" is better than "Do you get on with the other staff?" If he says "I don't", then luck is on your side and you have something to get to grips with; if he doesn't get on with the others and he says he does then you have to think of another question to get you out of a spot.

Keep questions simple. Just as simple sentences are more easily read so are simple questions more easily answered. Some people when interviewing get carried away by their own eloquence and make statements rather than ask questions. They think that if they add a question mark to the end of a statement they have asked a question!

Ask one question at a time and make sure that it is answered thoroughly before proceeding. You may need to seek clarification on several secondary points before the person has explained himself adequately.

How you ask questions is important. The tone of voice, the look and gestures all play a part in talking and listening. Sometimes all that is necessary to encourage the person to continue talking is a nod of the head or a 'yes'. But do try to avoid developing into a perpetual head-nodder or a 'yes' person. We must constantly be alert to the possibility that some of our mannerisms may be irritating and cause distraction.

Look interested. A wandering eye is very off-putting and while it may be true that the sun is shining and you would rather be playing golf or swimming, reality says that you are in your office carrying out a counselling interview. Nothing gives the impression of interest as much as facial expression and the look in the eye. Some people do have difficulty looking other people in the eye and of course it certainly should not be a stare. But just as the counsellee can gain impressions about you from your expression and the look in your eyes, so can you about him.

Do not be misled, however, about eye contact. Some people are superstitious about this and believe that just as the face is the mirror of the soul, so the eyes are the windows of the soul, which can be lured out through the eyes by direct eye contact with another person. The roots of such beliefs are buried very deep in the heritage of some cultures.

One further point about questions in counselling, is that the counsellor endeavours to ask the client those questions which he could, and should, be asking for himself. He may not question himself because he is too emotionally bound to the problem to achieve the degree of objectivity necessary to do so. What you can do is to inject a sense of order and show him how to cut through the emotional tangles; from the way you ask questions he can begin to develop his own self-questioning technique.

COUNSELLING IS — EMPATHY
IT IS NOT — SYMPATHY

Empathy is a very over-used word and borders on jargon. As I see it, empathy is the ability to understand emotionally the feelings of the other person. Sympathy is being affected by the same feeling or feelings experienced by the other person. It is often difficult to make clear distinctions between words and this is one of those instances.

Both empathy and sympathy derive from the same root—compassion or pity. To try and bring out the difference between empathy and sympathy I want to link them with two other words which again are used a great deal—objective and subjective.

Objective really means the ability to remain impartial and not let one's own feelings intrude. Subjective means the opposite—that our own feelings have influenced our judgment; that we have become biased or even prejudiced.

It could be said that empathy is objective compassion while sympathy is subjective compassion. If the counsellor is to be objective and empathetic we need to look at how he can achieve this and, conversely, how subjectivity can so easily take its place.

There is no such thing as a permanent or absolute state of empathy; it is not a quality which can be acquired once and for all. It is never static, it fluctuates according to the situation and the person we are counselling. Sometimes our empathy is spot on, at others it would appear to be overshadowed and off-beam.

Staff counselling is particularly prone to the possibility of prejudice and bias because of a whole cluster of facts of which the manager is aware: he may be biased in favour of or against the counsellee. In a sense, the manager in this situation is like a juryman in a court who has heard some evidence which the judge declares inadmissible. He must not let what he heard influence his decision; if he does his objectivity will be affected and his judgment will be clouded.

Empathy may also be affected by experience. The closer our own experience has been, or is, to the client's, the more likely we are to share similar feelings; sympathy can so easily replace empathy if we become over-involved.

I do not want to give the impression that feelings should be denied in the quest for objectivity. There are times in counselling when the fact that you *do* feel the way you do, and show it, can be positively therapeutic. In the interview with Sheila Armstrong (see Part 3), Mrs Quinn shows her hurt and it is this which gets through to Sheila. The people we are counselling need to see that we are 'real', that we have feelings just like them and that what they say can bring pain or pleasure to us. They also need to be assured that, in spite of the pain they may have caused us, we still accept them, and are prepared to continue to work with them to try to help them resolve their problems.

Involvement — Over-involvement

Would-be counsellors are frequently admonished not to become involved with their clients as this will interfere with their objectivity and empathy. My own feeling is that people who are afraid to become involved never achieve anything. What I think people mean when they say this is that we should be careful about becoming *over-involved:* over-involvement can cause us to lose objectivity, as we tend to become engulfed within the emotions of the other person. Most nurses, early in their training, learn the lesson of not becoming over-involved. Some, however, do not; and a part of them seems to die whenever a patient dies or they feel the pain the patient is experiencing. They have become overwhelmed by sympathy and pity. Would this have had a bearing on the student who discontinued training? (page 29).

If the counselling relationship is built on give and take, there has to be involvement but it is *objective involvement.* Involvement, which derives from understanding and insight and not from an internal need within the counsellor, is productive and constructive.

Sometimes it may be necessary, for the growth of the counsellor, for him to become over-involved. It is doubtful if there are many who have not, at some time, become deeply over-involved with a particular client and, as a consequence, have become overwhelmed and engulfed by the problem. It is difficult to explain why this happens but it can be a positive learning experience for both, if handled correctly.

Some people need the experience of becoming deeply involved, over-involved, with another person in order to fulfil something within themselves. There is the sense that the unknown is always terrifying and if we have never been over-involved we may be afraid of becoming involved at all, lest we become swamped by our own feelings. When we have become so deeply involved with another person that we plumb emotional depths never before touched, we are in a better position to know where our limits are.

Over-involvement is painful and calls for a radical re-appraisal of our attitudes, emotions and responses to other people. If, as I suggest later, (page 68) we have an understanding 'mentor', who is skilled in counselling, we can turn over-involvement into a positive learning experience. The fear of becoming over-involved may act as a barrier to any

43

counselling but if it happens, and we are able to turn into victory what at the time may seem like a defeat, we shall no longer be afraid of involvement and our counselling will take on a new dimension.

COUNSELLING IS — ENABLING
IT IS NOT — PERSUADING

These two words are not exactly antonyms but as far as counselling is concerned they are as opposite as the polar regions.

The reason counselling is being carried out is that one person has a problem, a difficulty, a dilemma, an obstacle to overcome and he cannot find the way through, cannot see a solution or the way out. We have already seen that the problem may either be personal or arise from work, but it is also reasonable to assume that a difficulty in one area of life will, to some extent, influence all others.

We have also examined the premise that the manager cannot ignore the problems of his staff, particularly when it can be clearly demonstrated that such problems have a detrimental effect on performance. Neither can he ignore and refuse to try to help the staff member who asks for help in dealing with personal problems, even although up to that moment performance has not been visibly affected.

If the only difference between staff counselling and any other form of counselling is in the focus, then the manager who counsels his staff does so using universally accepted concepts and principles. One of these concepts is that the counsellor is an enabler, a facilitator who assists the client to cut through the tangles, helps him to marshal his inner resources and emotional reserves to work towards a solution.

The fact that counselling, in whatever sphere, is based on common foundations, does not mean that there is only one method or approach. A possible danger in teaching any subject is that those being taught will be tempted to apply, without discrimination, the techniques and methods they have observed the teacher using. What they have failed to do, and what the teacher has possibly failed to emphasise, is how difficult it is for one person to model his approach exclusively on that of another person. The further one moves away from mechanical skills and crafts (where teacher and student carry out identical processes), towards conceptually based skills, such as counselling, the more inappropriate it is for the student's approach to be a replica of the teacher's.

Before one person can apply something, that which he has learned must be internalised, so that it becomes an integral part of his personality. When facts, ideas, principles and concepts are fused together within the individual's total experience then, and only then, can he begin to apply what he has learned in such a way that it emerges as experience and not just theory.

A skilful teacher, like a wise parent, will teach his students in such a way that each one will be encouraged to develop his own unique personality. The teacher provides the foundations; what the student then builds, to a large extent, rests with him.

What managers must do, in their quest for counselling skills, is not to concentrate exclusively on models or techniques but to internalise the basic concepts and principles which are common to all forms of counselling. When these concepts and principles are fused together and become an integral part of the personality, counselling practice will be established on a firm foundation.

Try not to adopt any one person's approach wholesale; many people have a great deal to offer; take what you can from them and make certain that what you acquire fits your basic personality. Never lose sight of the fact that you are unique and that certain methods and approaches may not fit you *in their entirety*. In other words, do not try to be someone you are not, but recognise and build upon your own strengths; but always remain yourself. In this way you will make certain that counselling is not something superficial but that it springs from deep within you.

Persuasion

Counselling is not persuading or prevailing upon or overcoming the resistance of another person, or wearing him down, or 'bringing him to his senses'. Persuasion is in direct conflict with at least one principle of counselling—the right of the individual to choose for himself his course of action. If the counsellor were to persuade the client to go a certain way, make a certain choice, there could be a very real danger of the whole affair backfiring in the face of the counsellor and resulting in further damage to the client.

This concept of self-direction, based on the freedom of the individual, is the touchstone of the non-directive approach to counselling but is present in most others. The basis of the principle is that any pressure which is brought to bear on the individual will create or increase conflict and so hamper exploration. We all know from our own experience, particularly with our parents or teachers, that any attempt to persuade us to adopt or pursue a certain course of action which may not tally with what we want, may cause certain things to happen!

If we have a high regard for the persuader or are afraid of him, we may swallow our resentment and capitulate. If we are continually forced into this situation, although outwardly compliant, a build-up of resentment within us is inevitable. The end-result is that the resentment will cause a rift in the relationship, or the person may become so compliant that he is completely dominated and unable to exercise his own choice in anything.

Another course of action would be for the persuaded to outwardly comply then go his own way, surreptitiously. Yet another outcome of persuasion is that the individual persuaded against his will would do what was expected of him but half-heartedly. In this circumstance, failure is virtually predestined. There is of course the possibility that he may openly rebel. In such circumstances the persuader is likely to be heard saying plaintively, "I just cannot understand why he is like that; after all I have tried to do for him . . .".

All this applies equally in counselling. It is certainly true that the person being counselled may allow himself to be persuaded by the counsellor to a certain course of action because he holds him in high regard. Implicit in this is "He is wiser, more experienced than I am, therefore he *must* know what is best for me." A manager may be regarded with awe or, in some instances, fear, by his staff; if this is the case, they could be more easily persuaded; the desired results may not necessarily follow.

When a person is experiencing emotional conflict his reasoning powers are affected and he may agree to something which, in normal circumstances, he would reject. If this is so, it is not difficult to appreciate that when the conflict has passed, and his emotional balance is partially, if not completely restored, he may then reject that to which he was persuaded to agree.

Advice

Advice-giving is closely bound up with persuasion and the two could very well be considered together.

Many people consider counselling as giving advice. To a certain extent this is true but there are qualifications. When the counsellor assists the client to explore the problem and puts before him all the pros and cons and suggests possible courses of action, he is advising.

If he has listened to the client and has heard accurately what has been said, the various points for and against one or several courses of action which he puts before the client, will be those towards which he feels the client has already started to move. It is certainly true that the counsellor may introduce some new thoughts or avenues to be explored; "Have you considered doing it this way?" could never be interpreted as persuasion but it is certainly advice.

When the counsellor lays before the client the possible consequences of a suggested course of action, he *is* advising but, and this is the difference, he is not saying, "This is what you should do." There is a difference between that and "This is what you could do." The essential difference is in the words 'could' and 'should'; the one is permissive, the other implies duty. If the counsellor gives only one course of action and says, "That is what I think you should (or ought to) do" he is using persuasion to have his advice accepted.

There are many occasions, of course, when one person *can* give advice with impunity. A store assistant will tell a customer that in order to achieve a satisfactory finish on painted woodwork, he should prepare it in a certain way. Having listened to the expert opinion, the customer is then perfectly at liberty to accept or reject the advice.

Another sales assistant may tell a lady customer that a particular dress . . . suits madam very well" implying that 'madam' would be well advised to buy it. This however, is a matter of opinion and taste, both of which are influenced by many factors.

The person who comes for counselling with a personal problem may hope for concrete advice, like the customer who wants to paint a door. There may be one perfect way to paint a door but how it is actually done rests entirely with the individual.

The astute sales assistant, trained in matching colours and outfits, will be able to produce a variety of dresses which, according to fashion, could suit the customer. She will help the customer to explore each item fully and the really skilled assistant will not willingly allow the customer to make an unsuitable choice. The advice she gives will be something like, "That colour suits your hair (or face, figure, etc.)" She may also advise her that the price is ". . . just a little high", or ". . . specially reduced". The skilled saleswoman will never apply undue pressure—she knows that this will often cause the customer to become annoyed, resulting in a lost sale.

Counselling is like that in many ways. Advice can be given, and is generally accepted without question, where practical issues only are involved. Even here the advice given may not always be acted upon because the emotional element, although small, has probably been overlooked.

Staff counselling may involve more elements of advice-giving than personal counselling, especially where performance is involved. If a person's performance is below par, it is clearly within the manager's role to help that individual towards an improvement. The person whose performance is not up to standard certainly needs to be told, and he may also have to be advised how this improvement may be achieved. If his performance is suffering because of a personal problem it is to be hoped that the manager can help him improve his performance and thus relieve some of the pressure on other parts of his life.

It is probably true that most people do not distinguish very clearly between advice-giving and 'true counselling' in which direct advice-giving features very little. Nurses are generally competent when giving advice on health or clinical matters. The nurse faced with "What should I do with this cut (bruise, ulcer or whatever)?" would be listened to, and her advice acted upon without more ado. The same nurse, faced with "Nurse, I'm having trouble with my husband (child, neighbours or whatever), what should I do?", may well use the same approach, quickly sum up the situation (diagnosis) and offer a solution (treatment). I would suggest that this could backfire. We can give practical advice but where social or personal issues are involved, advice is rarely appropriate.

Advice-giving on personal aspects of life is fraught with dangers and generally arises from a desire to assert oneself as being 'right'. In reality, we are trying to persuade the other person that the way *we* have solved a problem, or would solve it, is the way for him. Such an attitude is rarely constructive and the client could very well say, "I was persuaded to accept what turned out to be bad advice." Don't let yourself be accused of this.

COUNSELLING IS – EXPLORATION
IT IS NOT – MANIPULATION

Sam, who had just started what looked to be a fairly long course of counselling said to me, "Bill, tell me what is going to happen, where will we end up?" My reply was that I did not know any more than he did; I had never been that way before. I knew from past experience that certain things could happen, but in a way it was like two people setting out on an exploration with a very crude map. The difficulties they would face may be similar to other experiences they have had, but new approaches may have to be adopted.

This illustration helped Sam to see that both of us were in this together and the final result would emerge from our combined efforts and working together. He could see that I did not have all the answers and that I did not know which way we should go.

I think he asked this question to test me out. He may have asked it in order to establish more precisely our relationship. If I had presumed to 'know', it would have placed him in the position of following, of being led. This feeling of inequality could jeopardise any constructive work.

The person who comes for counselling has already placed himself in a position of inequality by admitting that he cannot cope. The fact that you are in a position to counsel places you, in his eyes, in the position of helper. It also implies that you have a skill or knowledge or emotional strength which he does not possess. This inequality (at least in his perception) may create a barrier between you.

Any sense of inequality can be reduced if it is made quite clear that the only reason we are in a position to counsel is because we are not involved in the problem. These feelings may further be reduced if we are able to say that at times we too need someone to speak to about the problems *we* encounter.

For instance I say that I often need to seek help from someone else, especially when the clients I am dealing with are passing through particularly sticky patches, when movement forward seems to have come to a stop. The fact that you need to consult a 'mentor' need not interfere with your relationship if the question of confidentiality is clarified.

Exploration implies that the counsellor does not know the way; that it is a joint expedition. It also implies that the outcome cannot be known any more than explorers tracing the river to its source can know. In their journey towards the source there will be difficulties and sometimes dangers to be met with and circumvented; promising avenues will lead nowhere and steps will have to be painfully retraced. In spite of all this, the drive forward will continue, compelled by the search for the truth. Just so in counselling; together, and always together, client and counsellor explore various avenues, searching for a solution or solutions to the problem. Unlike the explorers (although not unlike the psychoanalyst), the counsellor and client are not so much seeking 'the source' but 'a' solution which will produce a satisfactory resolution.

Guidance

Exploration in counselling is linked with guidance, although some would dispute this. I hope that what I have said thus far about exploration will clearly demonstrate that when I talk about guidance, it is not meant in the sense of a 'guide'—one who knows the way. It is certainly true that the counsellor may have been along similar ways with other clients but every journey is unique.

What I mean by guidance is that the counsellor will be there to point out possible pitfalls and dangers, help the client over difficult patches and give encouragement when enthusiasm flags. He is someone on whom the client can lean when he feels weak.

In staff counselling the manager is giving guidance to his staff when he discusses ways and means of achieving an improvement in performance.

A young secretary, Sally, responsible for the enquiries office in a Social Services department, was constantly in a muddle; could never find anything quickly and repeatedly mislaid important papers. It was obvious she lacked method and organisation. The office supervisor discussed this with her and discovered that she was exactly like this in her private life. She also discovered that although she had covered the usual secretarial skills in her training, office management had been sadly neglected. She thought it would be a good idea to allow Sally time off to attend a short course in office management and procedure. This she did and when she returned it was obvious that the course had done some good; she was more able to cope (although this part of her work was always weak).

There does not appear to be anything momentous about this illustration but the majority of counselling situations *are* undramatic and are quite capable of being carried out by the majority of people.

Another point about exploration and guidance is that the counsellor must keep pace with the client—'in tandem' is a term often used to describe this; it implies a keeping together, a united effort. To maintain this close position, it is essential for the counsellor to keep in constant touch with the client's feelings; this is achieved by effective listening.

Manipulation

You will have gained the distinct impression that counselling, as I have described it, is not manipulation. There are some definitions of manipulation which could be loosely thought of as guidance, but what counselling definitely *is not* is 'unfair influence'. Manipulation in this sense means something underhand, a plot, duplicity.

When one person persuades another to do or attempt something (even though it may be against his better judgment or wishes), he does so usually in such a way that the person realises what is happening. The person who manipulates another to do what *he* wants, does so subversively, not in the open, and (this is the essential difference) usually for some personal gain and not in the best interests of the other person.

Do you think the Ward Sister mentioned on page 27 could be accused of manipulation? The dividing line between manipulation and seeking ways and means to resolve a problem may not always be easily seen, but the deciding factor must be *who benefits?* In the case already referred to it was clearly not the Sister who benefited directly but the whole staff, Jean and Mary and of course, ultimately, the patients.

Counsellors may be accused of manipulation, and indeed some students of counselling subscribe, initially, to the idea that the counsellor manoeuvres the client so adroitly that he agrees with what the counsellor proposes as if he himself had thought of it. This can be done and it is a very subtle means of ensuring that the client takes the direction which the counsellor feels is right. He can do this by loading the exploration in favour of the direction he has chosen, by limiting the exploration to one avenue or by putting forward all the difficulties against any other choice.

The counsellor can make suggestions which manipulate the client's feelings. For example, the client may be passing through a difficult time with his girl friend. The counsellor, in the belief that it would be best for him to end the relationship, introduces a whole gamut of moral issues which make the client feel so guilty that he severs the relationship in an inappropriate manner which leaves both him and the girl feeling resentful.

Very often people who counsel will manipulate the client's feelings to satisfy their own emotional needs. It is probably true to say that we all counsel to get something out of it, but the majority of us have enough awareness of our own emotional needs not to let them overshadow our counselling. In the above examples of manipulation, when referring to 'the counsellor', I mean anyone doing counselling; I would not want to imply that counsellors who have undergone training would be guilty of this sort of manipulation; but neither would I want to suggest that those who have not received such a training would be any more guilty. Manipulation of any kind is caused by underlying motives.

The manager, when counselling his staff, must also be watchful that his own emotional needs do not intrude to the extent that he could be accused of manipulation. It is not always easy to detect when we have moved from exploration to manipulation but, as I have already said, a great deal depends on motives. If the counsellor is not clear when he is manipulating, the client will be, although he may not use that word. He may not realise at the time what is happening but when the session has ended, and he has time to reflect, his feelings are likely to be something like ". . . the cunning (and a suitable expletive), so that's what he was after. I won't trust him again."

The manager could possibly be forgiven for trying to manipulate his staff in order to get the job done. If, in the process, people's feelings are hurt, the response is likely to be the same, resulting in mistrust and a build-up of resentment, which could interfere with the smooth running of the department.

If the motive is personal glory and kudos, manipulation will be resented; if the manager is motivated by organisational or department satisfaction, he will operate within a different framework and will be sensitive enough of the feelings of others not to hurt them. If he does, he will also be sensitive enough to realise it and to quickly make amends.

53

COUNSELLING IS — ACCEPTANCE
IT IS NOT — REJECTION

Much of what has gone before in this chapter has prepared the way for the last of the two paired concepts—acceptance and rejection.

On page 14, acceptance was touched on related to caring. I said that it does not mean condoning the behaviour of the client. In essence it is like the woman who, in spite of everything, still loves the husband who beats her, deprives her of money and is unfaithful to her. She could not in any sense approve of what he *does* but she accepts him *as he is.* Something within him still holds her to him, although many people would 'advise' her to cut loose from him. Nothing he *does* will change her attitude which springs from an understanding heart. She will attempt to understand what it is that makes him behave the way he does and this understanding issues from a well of caring. It is also possible that she is afraid of facing the consequences of leaving him, of facing life without him.

The counsellor may not have quite the same feelings portrayed above, but basically they spring from the same well—of caring. The client is likely to approach counselling with feelings of rejection although the intensity of these feelings will depend, to a large extent, on the nature of the problem which has caused the necessity for counselling. People do not always find it easy to approach another person for help—to admit that they are not masters of their own ships. This feeling alone prevents many people from seeking help. There is also the feeling that counselling will somehow interfere with independence. These feelings, coupled with the emotions aroused by the actual problem, may all contribute to the feelings of rejection.

The problem itself is another reason which may make a person hesitate to seek help. If the problem is personal or behavioural (as distinct from essentially practical) the fact that he admits this would seem to set him apart as being different from other people; rejection is again likely to be experienced. If the problem involves other people—family, for instance—there are many moral issues with which he may feel at variance. He may have transgressed the law in some way, thus in his eyes he is a 'criminal'. The client who rejects and condemns criminals, for instance, and himself transgresses, may reject himself or fear that the counsellor will reject him as he (the client) rejected others.

These feelings of guilt, unworthiness, shame and so on, all tend to build up in his mind and shout at him "He will not accept you." In reality, the client cannot accept himself; he has ceased to respect himself, to have a regard for himself. A person in this abject state is going to find it difficult to believe that the counsellor *can* accept him—warts and all. No volume of words could reassure him; in this instance empathy conveys what words never could.

A child ran across the road in front of a bus and narrowly escaped being hit; the mother grabbed him, shook him and said "You stupid, stupid child." Was the child stupid? If the mother had said "That was a stupid thing to do", would this have been different?

Tom, the laundry employee, severely damages his machine; would you say "You careless, irresponsible man", or "That was a careless, irresponsible thing to do"?

Very often we judge, criticise and reject the person instead of judging, criticising and rejecting his behaviour. Does the mother in the example above, who persistently tells the child that he is 'stupid', run the risk of producing a 'stupid' child? If the manager berates the employee as being 'careless and irresponsible', does he run the risk of creating just that?

Both of these illustrations point to the possibility that the way we regard people can influence their behaviour. The logical conclusions in these illustrations is for the child to believe that he is stupid, and for the employee to be so resentful that he continues to behave carelessly and irresponsibly. In essence, both the mother and the manager are showing rejection.

I do not mean that they should not have shown anger (or fear, in the case of the mother); nor do I mean that the child and Tom should escape correction, for both should realise the errors of their ways. When we criticise *the person* instead of *the behaviour,* we close the door upon creating a positive learning experience out of what has happened.

When a person comes for counsel, and possibly has to admit that he has done something stupid, or careless or irresponsible, he may not be able to separate, in his mind, behaviour from personality. He may have convinced himself that he *was* stupid, careless and irresponsible. If this is how he feels about himself he is also likely to fear that the counsellor could not accept him; just as he rejects himself (not his behaviour), he fears the counsellor will do likewise.

The mother no doubt responded as she did from fear; the manager from frustration (and possibly from fear of what *his* boss might say). It would not be easy for either the mother or the manager to sit down and counsel the respective offender because heightened emotions have created a barrier. We now see a double rejection in operation and there is only one way out—someone must apologise, but who?

It is not necessary, or even desirable, to apologise for being upset over behaviour, but what needs to be rectified is the assault on the personality. If managers accept the premise that it is possible to accept the person without accepting his aberrant behaviour, counselling, when it takes place, will be launched from a sure base.

If, on the other hand, the manager cannot separate the person from his behaviour, he stands in very real danger of rejecting the counsellee totally because he feels there is nothing worthwhile to which he can relate. If the manager relates to the person and not to the behaviour he is showing acceptance of something worthy within the person. If he perceives the other as 'bad', because of what he has done, he has judged the person and not his behaviour and having judged, he has passed sentence—rejection.

If anyone is to be helped to change his behaviour which is causing concern, to himself or to others, he must be helped to make this change from within. If we can believe that there is a spark of good within everyone, it will help when faced with a person who, to all outward appearances, can do nothing right. If the counsellor can make contact with this 'good' spark, a great deal may be achieved.

Much of what takes place in counselling tends to centre around the question 'why'? Very often the client does not know why he does what he does or why he is what he is, and a great deal of time may be wasted trying to establish the 'why' and the 'how' of what has caused the specific change in behaviour. When you try searching for *the* root cause you move from counselling into the realm of psychoanalysis.

It is essential to explore the problem which has brought the staff member and you together—that is the 'why' of the here-and-now—the problem; for instance Tom who has damaged his laundry machine. It may emerge that he has a deep-seated personal problem and has kept silent. If the manager accepts him as a man with a problem (rather than a 'problem man') he will demonstrate to Tom a certain level of understanding and acceptance.

Instead of an endless (and usually fruitless) search among the archives of the client's mind for the missing psychological link which has caused the problem, far better to help him to concentrate on ways and means of making some change in his behaviour. For it is this, some change in his behaviour, how-ever small, which will indicate to him (and you) that his problem is soluble and will provide hope of further gains.

Unfortunately some people, when counselling, emulate psychoanalysts and concentrate on the source rather than on the behaviour, but this is like a gardener trying to erradi-cate perennial bindweed from his garden. He can spend a life-time digging, from January to December, picking out little bits of the root only to discover when summer comes that for every bit of root he has dug up, many more have escaped his eye and the bindweed will cock a horticultural snook at him as it twists its way merrily up everything in sight.

Another approach would be to admit that, short of cover-ing the garden in concrete, the roots will remain but that whenever the first tendrils appear they will be cut down. This continual cutting down will at least keep other plants free from the insidious creeper.

It may be true that Tom has some problems, and if by talking them over his anxiety is reduced his behaviour will be influenced for the better. It may be, however, that his problem stems from a deep-rooted personal difficulty which causes him to indulge in irresponsible acts. If the manager concentrates on this and ignores the behaviour he could discover that he has a laundry full of wrecked machines! The manager could take a leaf from the gardener's book and seriously consider what can be realistically achieved.

Unresolved Conflicts

One last word must suffice for this subject of acceptance. I said that some people feel rejected because of their feelings about others; this applies equally to the counsellor. People who counsel are likely to experience difficulty with certain clients who make emotional demands involving areas of unresolved conflicts (or hang-ups, in modern parlance) in the lives of the counsellors. These unresolved conflicts cause us to erect barriers behind which we retreat to safety. We may, therefore, reject the client outright, making him feel guilty in the process, or attempt to deal with him on a purely intellectual level and accomplish very little.

John, an accountant, came to see the personnel manager to ask for his advice. He began by telling Mr Smart that he found difficulty concentrating on his work and was constantly having to repeat much of it; this was worrying and time-consuming. Mr Smart, at this stage, showed himself to be an effective listener and encouraged John to explore why. After some time John, looking ashamed, admitted that he knew in his heart-of-hearts the true cause—he was having a clandestine affair with another woman.

At this stage Mr Smart virtually 'dried up', looked embarrassed and said, "I'm afraid I can't help you, I don't want to be involved with this sort of thing." Mr Smart felt very shaken when John left; he, himself, was having an extra-marital affair. Small wonder he could not help!

This illustration is fairly straightforward and easily understood, but some of our unresolved conflicts are more deep-rooted than this. Whenever you attempt to help another through counselling, you run the risk of having some of these hidden areas brought into focus. If such conflicts are resolved you will move forward freely without fear. Such freedom can only prove beneficial to your own well-being and bring a new vitality to your counselling.

SUMMARY

At the start of this chapter I said that very few things in life are black or white and that when considering counselling it is difficult to keep subjects in water-tight compartments. As you have read through the chapter both these statements should be self-evident.

Part of the skill in counselling is to hold a number of different strands together without getting them tangled. Sometimes, however, they do become tangled. It may seem that neither you nor the client has understood what the other has been trying to say, and there may be times when both of you go away feeling, "Is it all worth it?" If this happens, do remember that most people engaged in counselling feel like this at some time. In the end, however, tangles do become unravelled and understanding dawns.

Some of the concepts and ideas and the basic philosophy may sound a bit strange to you, and it may be only after several readings that some of what I have said clicks into place. Some points may remain obscure until brought to light during counselling.

This and That –
A Miscellany of Ideas

It is difficult for me to give a definitive heading to this chapter to indicate its contents. What I have done is to bring together several different topics which all have a bearing on the counselling process. Some of them have been introduced in the preceding chapters; here they will be expanded.

I have frequently found it necessary to search for ways to help clients and students understand various points about the process. Sometimes one may be asked something which until then has been taken for granted. The question cannot be ignored and as an answer is searched for (because it may not always spring instantly to mind), one is led along new roads of discovery.

THE GROWTH POINT PROCESS

The first of these ideas I would like to discuss is what I have come to call the Growth Point Process.

Several years ago I was working with Sam (page 49), in what was a fairly intensive counselling relationship. He was a man of high intelligence who was experiencing difficulty in being able to relate to people. A consequence of this was that he had turned his back on his vocation as a musician and had great difficulty settling to any kind of work.

When we had been together for several weeks (he came weekly for one hour) he began to experience what the majority of people experience who are having on-going counselling—emotional upheaval. At one stage he said, "Bill, I'm beginning to wonder if it is all worth it, I seem to be more emotionally upset now than when I started; I feel I'm drowning." (This is a very common feeling.) It was certainly true that he was experiencing turbulence because of his internal conflict which resulted from conflicting values.

He expressed his doubts about continuing and said, "What have we achieved?" We looked critically at what had taken place and highlighted about six distinct areas in which some progress had been made. These six areas, I told him, were like little islands in the midst of his troubled emotional sea. When he felt he was floundering he could stand on one of them and regain his emotional strength, until he was rested enough to resume his quest. He could stand upon each of these areas in which progress had been made, one by one and, as it were, claim them as his by right of possession. He could not deny that progress had been made; that was real and solid and would provide him with something positive by which to gauge his progress. When we next met he said he had given this a great deal of thought and agreed that it was true and in the intervening week had to say to himself on several occasions, "I am standing on what I have accomplished, I am not going to drown, I am going to survive."

Each of these little islands had become a point of growth, and as they continued to grow, some would eventually coalesce to make one substantial territorial gain. As each growth point expanded, so the amount of time in which Sam was left struggling in the waterways of his emotions would be reduced. In his case there were a number of these growth points which never did expand a great deal, (at least during counselling, although on subsequent contact with him there was evidence that the process continued for some considerable time after we parted); others did, however, and it was in these areas of his life that turmoil gave way to peace.

This anecdote emphasises an important principle which I might well have overlooked if Sam had not forced it upon me.

Always make sure you keep the client in touch with what is happening. I had told Sam at the outset that he would most probably experience something like this and thought that having issued the warning once, that would be sufficient. But obviously I had not gauged the depth of his feelings. His use of the word 'drowning' says a great deal, does it not? I think probably I used the illustration of the islands because he was interested in everything connected with the sea, and I felt he would readily grasp the connection.

My experience with Sam alerted me to how essential it is to say something not once but many times and to keep on repeating it until we are certain it has registered. It also teaches a valuable lesson in always making sure that progress is duly noted, as an encouragement to both client and counsellor.

When Sam and I parted company he wrote a letter in which he said, "When we started meeting I didn't know what to expect; what little I did know was gleaned from books, T.V. or radio. What threw me was when you said right at the beginning that you did not have any answers for me but that together we would search for ways in which I could solve my own problems. I felt a bit cheated by this and wondered if you really knew what you were talking about. I apologise for that.

I cannot begin to tell you the awful feeling I had that I was being swallowed up by my problems; all I knew is that each time I came to you seemed like the only bright spot in my week and when I left I wondered how I could survive the next week.

At that stage I was pretty weak and low and needed your strength. Now, looking back on the experience, I would liken it to setting out on a sea voyage. For years I had lived secure in my little harbour being tossed to and fro but not too drastically. When you and I set out together (which is how you put it) I saw you as the pilot, and although we passed through some very stormy waters, and I thought I was going under, you were there.

There came a time when I know we turned around and started back for harbour. Now I have entered but things look different; things which used to frighten me no longer do: I am at peace."

This is not a success story. Sam continued to experience difficulties on and off for several years. You may not be in a position to carry out counselling over a long period of time as I did with Sam, but whenever counselling is undertaken, the client is likely to feel something like this, and provided you keep in touch with his feelings you too can help to identify growth points which will encourage him and you.

RESISTANCE

Resistance is the second point I wish to consider. Many people who require counselling also experience resistance to it. This paradox is something which every counsellor must recognise and accept. As a general rule the resistance is not personal, although it is possible that counselling in the work environment may engender more personal resistance than counselling elsewhere because of the degree of pre-counselling involvement.

The client experiences resistance, in the first instance, because of what is happening within him; conflict of any kind creates its own resistance. If we look at the case of Jean and Mary (page 27) we can assume that because of their antagonism towards one another they would have been markedly resistant to the Sister if she had attempted to 'counsel' them. That she was using counselling skills was evident, but she did not actually sit them down and say "Let's talk about this problem"; she focussed on something essentially practical; her tactic worked.

Another reason for resistance is linked with the feelings to which I have already drawn attention—of not being master of his own ship. Personal disappointment, fear, resentment are feelings which are all liable to be present. He may realise that his personal life is in chaos and that his work performance is suffering, and all this makes him feel guilty. Guilt causes us to anticipate censure which leads to a build-up of resistance.

Anticipated change may also cause resistance. The person with a problem is put in the position of having to change some aspect of his behaviour. (There is of course the possibility that in fact it is not he, the client, who needs to change his behaviour but other people who have somehow manipulated him into the situation of believing that he is the one who should change.) He may agree that change is required, indeed is desirable, but paradoxically he resists the change. In a sense this is related to his perception of the counsellor. If he sees him as someone who can enforce change (and remember that many people have some strange ideas of what counselling actually is!) he may show more resistance than if he considers him as a person who will enable him to make his own changes.

If the person does not accept that he has a problem he will be almost certain to be resistant.

The Ward Sister could not get on with Liz, one of her Staff Nurses. They were constantly at loggerheads and the Sister was convinced that Liz needed counselling and arranged for the Nursing Officer to counsel her. (The Nursing Officer had only been recently appointed; an external appointment.)

During the discussion the Nursing Officer listened to Liz's point of view which she put logically and lucidly. It appeared that the Sister had her 'pets' and Liz was not one of them. The Nursing Officer decided to take a few more soundings before taking further action. In this case Liz could have been quite justified if she were resentful and resistant; she may well have said that it was not she but the Sister who needed counselling.

This illustration underlines the well-known fact that things are seldom what they appear to be.

If you remember that all clients may experience resistance you will be prepared for it when it shows itself, possibly in antagonism, anger, rudeness or any other negative feeling. If you attempt to push the client ahead too fast, or if you talk too much and are negative in your approach you can create or increase resistance.

The client is most likely to be labouring under strong emotions, and it is reasonable to assume that it would be difficult for him to concentrate on a constructive appraisal of the situation until he has been allowed to ventilate such feelings. The prudent counsellor will discern the early-warning signs of heightened emotions and permit, and indeed encourage, the client to give vent to them. Just as effective ventilation will rid a room of stale odours, so ventilation of negative feelings will reduce resistance.

Resistance may manifest itself at any time during counselling. It could become apparent in the way the client blocks what the counsellor is putting forward; instead of considering what is being said he objects to it and argues against it without consideration. This may be due to the fact that the counsellor has touched a trigger spot, a tender area, a hidden something he does not want to discuss. If the counsellor says something like, "I seem to have touched a tender spot, perhaps you would rather not discuss it at this stage", he is telling the client quite clearly that he has recognised his feelings, that he is still alongside him but he is also leaving the way open in his "at this stage" for the client to discuss it when he is ready and if he so desires.

Resistance does not emanate exclusively from the client; this would put the relationship on an unequal basis. I have indicated elsewhere, in the illustrations of Mr Stevens and Mr Smart (pages 30 and 58) that the counsellor is just as prone to experience resistance as is the client. In every counselling interview the counsellor's own emotions, attitudes, opinions and beliefs are brought sharply into focus and at any given moment he may discover that some sacrosanct attitude or belief has been brought into conflict with an opposing attitude or belief of the client.

On one occasion a client's religious beliefs clashed with mine and before I was aware of what was happening we had entered into a theological debate—very interesting but not at all constructive. (The more passionately we 'believe' in something, the more liable we are to experience resistance when faced with an opposing belief.) When we had gone on for several minutes in this intellectual but sterile discussion, we both stopped (probably for breath!) and he said "I caught you on the hop then, didn't I?" We cleared the air by having a good laugh at my expense.

HUMOUR IN COUNSELLING

This leads me to talk about humour in counselling. Some people have the idea that counselling is deadly serious (for serious read dull), a matter of life and death, and that humour would be as out of place here as in a funeral parlour. Not a bit of it: don't be afraid of enjoying a joke together.

Laughter is a good medicine but like all remedies it can be abused and produce undesired results. Laughter can be a very effective means of releasing tension, as everyone who has been faced with an irate spouse will testify. If husband and wife, who are both set full-sail on a collision course, *can laugh together,* the explosive element will be defused. The secret is laughing together, or one laughing at himself (or herself), *not the one laughing at the other.*

There are some people who laugh continually about all sorts of things; such people must be very difficult to live or work with. One conjectures that if they stopped laughing, their inner tensions would catch up with them and overwhelm them. Perhaps they need to laugh to prevent other people's tensions contaminating them.

What I would like to emphasise is: moderation in all things and that includes humour. Don't try to inject humour because you think it might be a good idea, and above all don't try to use it if it contradicts your basic personality. If you lack humour, don't try and ape the 'life and soul of the party'; accept yourself as you are. If you are the opposite type of person, who laughs at everything, do remember that your humour may jar the sensitive client who may feel that you are laughing at him or his problem. If, on the one hand you are humourless (although I doubt that such a person really exists), or on the other you constantly bubble over, you could profitably spend time looking at the positive and negative effects you could have on people including clients. Humour in counselling must be natural and used with as much empathy as any other communication.

THE MENTOR RELATIONSHIP

Several times I have mentioned the 'mentor relationship'; now would be an appropriate time to develop this theme.

From what I have said you will have realised that I believe that for counselling to be productive the counsellor must be continually moving forward towards increased understanding of himself in relation to other people. Time and time again he will be brought into contact with clients whose problems will awaken within him something which will create resistance or conflict *within that relationship and specific to it.* The client's difficulty will not be adequately resolved until the counsellor's own resistance or conflict is resolved. It is true that the client may seek help from other sources, but in this instance it would be the counsellor's personal development which would be retarded. When faced with a situation where your own emotions are thrown into turmoil, or where counselling appears to have reached stalemate, there are three courses of action which you can take. You can pull the blanket over your head and hope the problem will go away; work at it on your own or you can seek help.

In counselling we hope the client will achieve a degree of insight in order to see his problem more realistically. If insight is essential for the client, how much more is it essential for the counsellor? If it is necessary for the client to seek help from someone to work through his problem (if he had been able to work it out for himself, surely he would), it is equally important for the counsellor.

There is an element of truth in what people say: that you must have experienced something before you can really help others. This does not mean that the counsellor must have passed through an *identical* experience, but it is important that every counsellor has been the recipient in a helping relationship. Perhaps you can recall a time when you needed to talk with someone about your career prospects, or some difficulty related to work. Did you get the help you needed? Were you helped to resolve the difficulty? Can you remember trying to help someone else who obviously did not want your help? How did you feel? Trying to remember these feelings will help to put into perspective what I have to say.

Many people who counsel have personal experience of what it is like to be a client, and it has been this experience which has prompted them to become counsellors. Not everyone has had this first-hand experience and yet it is possible to experience similar feelings when it becomes necessary to seek the help of someone else during counselling.

The person in need of counselling has probably put off seeking help and has tried to work it out for himself, but to no avail—the problem is still there. He is bound to feel inadequate; that he should have been able to manage, can this other person really help? You may experience similar feelings when it is obvious that the counselling relationship has turned sour, that the other person is being difficult, resistant, hostile or whatever, and the initial problem has assumed more ominous proportions. It would be no more easy for you in this position to go to someone else for help than it is for the client to come to you. At that stage you, in your heart, know how the client feels. Oh yes, you will resist it, and rebel against it, but only if you submit to this experience, when it becomes necessary, will your counselling assume true empathy—heart knowledge will have replaced head knowledge.

In some circles this aspect of counsellor development is called 'supervision'; adequate enough, but I prefer to call it a 'mentor relationship'. If you refer to the dictionary differences between these two words, I'm sure you will see why I prefer 'mentor' to 'supervisor'.

The mentor will help the counsellor to resolve the difficulty which has arisen between himself and his client mainly because he can stand outside it and explore with the counsellor what is happening within: (a) the client; (b) the counsellor; and (c) the relationship between counsellor and client. The mentor will be able to use what happens between himself and the counsellor—the relationship—to point to what may be happening between the counsellor and the client; in the same way that the counsellor may be able to point out to the client that what happens between them may be similar to what happens between the client and other people. For the counsellor who has such a mentor relationship the potential for personal awareness is infinite. The counsellor who chooses to disregard such a relationship will lose out and eventually become ineffective in his counselling.

Counselling has a chain of influence; the client, counsellor and mentor all benefit from what takes place. The mentor's own personal awareness and skill are broadened with every different relationship. In the end the client must benefit, but he can only benefit if everyone sustains the process.

Staff counselling may present difficulties for the manager who does not have a 'designated' mentor (as professional counsellors, especially those under training or working within an established counselling agency, have) and yet he probably needs this support as much as the professional and, in some instances, due to lack of training, more so. If, however, he takes seriously the injunction contained in this section, he will seek out someone with whom he can develop such a relationship. This person may be another manager who is more skilled in counselling, a doctor, psychiatrist, social worker, probation officer or a counsellor in one of the other statutory agencies or voluntary organisations where counselling is carried out.

Do not underestimate this part of the counselling process. One of my most memorable experiences is when I was working with Sam.

There were certain aspects of this relationship which created anxiety in me and during discussion with my mentor (who was a psychiatrist colleague, and whom I had to approach for help) he put his finger on something which I had missed.

Sam was a lonely man, solitary but not unfriendly. I told my mentor that very often I felt I wanted to hold Sam, to comfort him. He said, "Like you would one of your sons?" That was precisely it. Sam evoked my paternal feelings and I remembered that several times I had thought of him as a little boy. I was helped to see that possibly I found it easier (and safer) to respond to male clients as if they were children rather than as adults. This session unlocked yet another emotional door leading to fresh discoveries about the way I interacted with people.

At my next meeting with Sam I related my experience (I am not suggesting that this is obligatory or necessary) and asked him if he had realised anything of this. He had not been aware of this precise feeling but on reflection he was not surprised; he did in fact often feel like a little boy—a lost little boy. I wondered aloud if this was how he came over to other people. He thought about this in the intervening week and said that possibly he did portray this lost little boy rather deliberately, knowing that it would evoke compassion. We discussed this and he began to see that some people responded to this feeling by rejection because they could not tolerate the 'lost little boy' in him when what they wanted was to relate to Sam 'the man'.

PARENTS AND TEACHERS

One of the possible difficulties of the mentor relationship is that it may have overtones of the parent/child or teacher/pupil relationships. These early relationships exert very powerful and pervading influences on our lives and the way we interact with people. The vestiges of these two similar, but different, relationships influence how readily we seek help and also determine our attitude towards the 'helper', be he the counsellor, from the client's standpoint, or the mentor from the counsellor's.

The counsellor who views the mentor through emotional eyes, bedimmed by an unsatisfactory parental or teacher relationship, is liable to experience difficulty, which may be one of the reasons for resistance. The experienced mentor (or counsellor dealing with the client) will use this relationship difficulty as a stepping-stone towards further development and will not permit it to become a stumbling-block.

MASTER AND SERVANT

The manager who engages in counselling his staff may also experience conflict from both parent and teacher relationships but also from the remnants of the master/servant relationship. I know that theoretically many of the old customs and practices related to master and servant have been swept away by a succession of reforms, but attitudes take longer to eradicate.

It is difficult to believe that the following attitude could be expressed in the last quarter of this century by a man who had not yet reached his fortieth birthday.

In a television programme about the countryside, a game-keeper was asked about his relationship with the estate owner. He said "I know my place and am quite happy to keep it that way. The master is always right, I would never dream of questioning him."

These words could have been lifted right out of any novel of a century ago.

The attitude of the 'master' is still evident from the way some employers and managers talk about their employees. It is also evident that many employees think of themselves as 'servants'.

If the client thinks of himself as a 'servant' (although he may never have put this into words), it is also possible that he will have a large reservoir of resentment which could stand in the way of constructive counselling even by a manager who in no sense displays attitudes of 'the master'. I would not suggest that all Dickensian master/servant relationships were bad or that all servants were ill-treated or exploited. Many people cared for their servants more than is evident today in some 'enlightened' organisations.

The fact is that the client who is before you may bear the resentment of generations of his forebears who *were* ill-treated and exploited, some worse than slaves. If this *is* his heritage he may bear resentment towards all people in authority. If his feelings were put into words they could be something like "I'll be servant to no man; no man will be master over me." Counselling such a client would present difficulties. If, however, the manager is careful to establish a satisfactory pre-counselling relationship with his staff he will have already demonstrated that there is a world of difference between being a manager and master, and employee and servant.

PLATEAUX

Frequently, especially during on-going counselling, progress appears to have stopped; little or nothing seems to be happening. This is similar to what I described earlier in the Growth Point Process, although there is no significant emotional upheaval to contend with.

When I first experienced this I discussed it with my mentor, and we could see no apparent reason why this should be; he said, however, that it was not unusual. He took me back over what had happened and the obvious progress which had been made. It just so happened that at about that time I was learning to touch-type and had experienced some difficulty gaining extra speed. An experienced typist with whom I discussed this said that most students experience the same difficulty but that with practice the speed would improve once the plateau was passed. Her use of the word 'plateau' brought back to my memory something from my psychology lectures about plateaux in the learning process, and as I re-read this I could see how it applied to counselling.

When a person is learning a new skill the learning does not take place in a straight line but in a series of uphill climbs followed by horizontal lines or plateaux, when, in the case of typing, the speed remains static. It is in this plateau stage where consolidation takes place. It is also the stage where discouragement frequently sets in because progress (which up to that time has been fairly rapid) has slowed down.

As I applied this to counselling, I could see that the client had made substantial gains; his upward climb had been quite marked and well-sustained. Now he was on a plateau, resting, gaining new psychological strength ready for the next phase. We took a closer look at the process thus far, the gains he had made and the differences, however small, such gains had made in his life.

I realised that we had both been in danger of trying to hasten the process and it was not until then that we had stopped to take stock. Any attempt on my part to push him could have created resistance because he was not yet ready to move on to the next stage. After one or two sessions, it became obvious from what he said that he was now ready.

Managers who are counselling their staff, because they have frequent, often daily, contact with them, may not readily detect progress when it is made—like parents who don't observe their children's physical growth. Very often it needs someone else to draw attention to the change.

When we speak of behaviour change we do not mean a radical over-night conversion, but a gradual movement towards the desired, acceptable behaviour. The change, when it does take place, may go unnoticed until someone says, "What has happened to Tom? He no longer jumps down my throat when I speak to him." It may be some time, however, before Tom is able to move from the safety of this particular plateau; only when he feels secure in the gains he has made will he have the confidence to move out and start on some other part of the problem which will take him upwards to another plateau.

REASSURANCE

How many times have you heard people say to others, "Oh don't worry, everything will turn out all right." This attempt at reassurance rarely reassures. I often wonder if it is really an attempt to reassure the speaker rather than the listener! You cannot give carte blanche reassurance in this way, and if you do, the person to whom you offer it will feel, instinctively, unable to trust your judgment.

It is much more reassuring if you accept the situation as it is presented without any attempt to diminish it or make it more than it is. The counsellor who accepts that the client is desperately worried about something, which many other people deal with adequately, is making contact with the client's feelings. It is these feelings, anxiety, fear, remorse and so on, which are interfering with his ability to cope. Acknowledging such feelings and allowing the client to explore them leaves the way clear for an exploration of the problem.

People who try to reassure others who feel guilty about some aspect of their behaviour with "Oh it can't be as bad as that" are again trying to diminish the problem in the eyes of the client. This must make him feel silly, to say the least; it is really implying that he does not know his own feelings. It may be true that the act, the omission, is not serious in its consequences, but to the client it *is* serious. How much more reassuring it is to listen instead of lightly dismissing it.

Reassurance is given more by what we *do* than what we *say*. The nurse, at the bedside of a patient, gives more reassurance by her presence and the touch of her hand than in an empty "Now, don't worry, everything will be fine", which she hopes the patient (or his relatives) will interpret as, "He's going to get better." Her competence, her manner are reassuring in themselves; her verbal reassurances could be a cover for her own anxieties.

The manager who has to counsel one of his staff because of some performance problem could fall into the same trap of verbal reassurance. He could try and diminish the seriousness of, for instance, the damage to the machine in the laundry. Far better that the employee realises the full significance of his default. I do not mean that he should be given a long list of how much it would cost to repair, the back-log of work, etc. but if he is led to discover the consequences for himself he will be less likely to feel resentful.

Having started off in this way, both manager and employee know precisely the nature of the case and it gives the manager a more positive base from which to work. His attitude will reassure the employee, that in spite of the seriousness, he is still prepared to help him towards a solution.

Reassurance also comes, as I said earlier, from helping the client to see what progress *has* been made. It also derives from the counsellor's manner and approach. The fact that he may admit he does not know all the answers, and that any solutions will arise from what both contribute, will help the client to realise that the counsellor respects what *he* is able to give. The confidence this generates will be more reassuring than a spate of words.

DISCIPLINE AND COUNSELLING

Are discipline and counselling antithetic? The manager may have to discipline his staff in one breath and counsel them with the next. This is fact, but there must be a clear distinction between the two procedures.

Where there is an established disciplinary procedure, as in the N.H.S., it is necessary to adhere strictly to that. One must never lose sight of the responsibility to the organisation and indeed to the individual whose best interests may very well be served by the manager demonstrating *his* loyalty and responsibility to the organisation which pays them both.

Very often the need for counselling arises out of what started as a disciplinary interview. Later we shall see how this applies in the case of Tom. There could be no doubt that damaging his machine warranted some disciplinary action, but the manager saw beyond the action and turned the interview into a counselling one.

The point about counselling and discipline is that the more we engage in counselling the more able we are to administer discipline effectively. The whole basis of discipline is founded on knowledge of the facts, understanding of the circumstances and an unbiased decision. Counselling develops the ability to analyse a situation and weigh up the pros and cons; it increases understanding of people, and the more understanding we have of them, and of ourselves, the more able we are to give an impartial decision.

I do not infer that the individual should not be confronted with the consequences of his action. There will always be those who will plead their case very plausibly that 'if only', and try to pass the blame to someone else in an attempt to escape their responsibilities. We would all like to be entirely blameless and feel that we were the victims of the mistakes of our parents, the way we were reared, our background, education or whatever. How convenient this would be; how soul-destroying!

It may be perfectly true that the client's childhood *was* traumatic, that he *did* have little love, that his father *was* a drunkard and beat him every night, but every individual must accept responsibility for his own behaviour. (There are

76

some, however, who because of 'diminished responsibility' cannot be held responsible; such people are usually cared for in Special Hospitals so it must be assumed that those of us outside such institutions must take responsibility for our behaviour and actions.) At some time or another we all make a conscious choice to pursue, or deviate from, a certain course of action. Counsellors must not collude with those who would shed responsibility for their behaviour by blaming circumstances or people.

When it comes to performance, the issue becomes a great deal clearer than it is in the nebulous realm of therapeutic counselling. Every employee is contracted to fulfil certain obligations, for which he is paid. If he does not fulfil these, he has deviated from his contract. When he does not measure up to the conditions of employment he needs to be told, and if necessary the disciplinary procedure must be invoked.

The manager who does not adhere to the established procedure of his particular organisation when he clearly should, is like the parent who neglects to exert authority over his children. But as I pointed out in the first chapter, every child needs to have his boundaries clearly defined: the employee needs to know where he stands, what is acceptable and what is unacceptable. The manager who neglects this part of his role has allowed his concern for the individual to interfere with his judgment of his responsibility to the organisation.

Never let it be said of you that you counsel, counsel, counsel but never discipline when it is patently obvious that you need to. This creates imbalance of the three resources mentioned in Chapter One.

APPRAISAL AND COUNSELLING

I will draw this chapter to a close by saying a few words about counselling in non-problem situations such as appraisal and career development.

For the manager who has established a satisfactory pre-counselling relationship with his staff, counselling will be accepted as an extension of that relationship. The counselling role is not donned like a robe and taken off just as easily to be hung up until it is next required. The attitudes and techniques necessary for effective counselling pervade the whole personality and influence the manager's response to his staff in many different ways.

Nowhere is this seen more clearly than in appraisal. Not all organisations have established appraisal systems; even where they are established not all adhere to the laid-down policy. Some managers, in organisations where there are no established systems, carry out their own appraisals.

We have already considered how to deal with performance problems which may be highlighted during appraisal, but there are often times when appraisal does not reveal deficiency. Appraisal is not just a looking-back; it is also a looking-forward, and it is here where counselling skills can help.

The person whose performance is adequate, or more than adequate, may still need counselling when his future career is discussed. The manager will have made an assessment of his performance and also his potential. From the reservoir of his experience he will help the other to explore different avenues. If he has become skilled in counselling people with problems, be they of performance or personal, he should find no difficulty in counselling his staff on their careers and future development.

PART 2

The Problem

CHAPTER 4

The Heart of the Problem – The Interview

THE NATURE OF THE PROBLEM

In Chapter Two we considered the characteristics of exploration in counselling; I want to concentrate in Part 2 on how to
explore the problem. Before we do that, however, we need to
examine the interview and some do's and don'ts.

If I were to ask you what the heart is, you would be likely
to say that it is a vital organ, situated in the chest, the function
of which is to pump blood around the body. That is a true
description, but in a philosophical sense, the heart has been
described as the seat of the affections and it is in this sense I
wish to think of it.

If we can accept the heart as being the seat of affections
(it doesn't really matter where we say the affections are
located, nobody really knows) we can also accept that within
the heart many feelings are present. Feelings perform the
function of keeping the personality in balance and this is
achieved by every feeling being counter-balanced by another—love/hate, joy/sorrow, peace/agitation, and so on.
It may be of help if you jot down as many pairs of feelings as
you can think of and put them under two broad headings:
positive and negative. Positive feelings are those which create
a state of well-being; negative feelings create unrest and
dis-ease.

THE EMOTIONAL HEART

Within the heart many feelings exist which for most of the time are kept in balance, and it would be logical to suggest that these feelings could be thrown out of balance with a resultant alteration in behaviour, albeit temporary. Most of us know the experience of being very 'up' and very 'down', full of happiness or full of despair. These states are usually produced by some external event. The majority of the time, however, we never reach these heights or depths, but the feelings, particularly negative ones, are easily triggered off by some difficulty, some problem. Not all problems are external and there are times in our lives when we have all experienced a disturbance of our feelings without any demonstrable cause.

We often use the expression 'getting to the heart of the problem' and I wonder if you can picture a heart with these feelings, which you have jotted down, scattered all around inside it. Each pair (and they must be thought of as inseparable) will be revolving in their own little orbits, maintaining balance between extremes to keep the individual in a state of relative well-being. For instance, he is relatively happy but not euphoric; jaded but not actually sad.

This state of equilibrium is our way of life for the most part until something comes along to disturb the feeling balance as the feelings are knocked out of their orbit. When this happens, one pair of feelings is likely to collide with others so that any one problem can affect many different feelings. The more feelings which are affected, knocked off balance, the more likely it is that the individual will produce disturbed behaviour.

Several times I have said that part of the counselling function is to help the client 'untangle' the problem and I would like to extend the illustration of the heart to show how the problem becomes tangled in the feelings.

Broadly speaking 'problems' can be classified into 'simple' and 'complex'. Simple problems are those which have only one strand, complex ones are multi-stranded. There is a certain truth, however, in the belief that no problem is simple, that when you start exploring, more strands are revealed. What I mean by 'strands' are demonstrable behaviour difficulties which in staff counselling influence performance.

On a piece of paper draw a heart and within it randomly place the pairs of feelings you jotted down. To one side draw a box marked 'problem' and from this box take a strand or thread so that it just pierces the outline of the heart. Now imagine that within the heart there is a great deal of movement (like in a washing machine); what would happen to the strand? It would very quickly become tangled up with the feelings, resulting in imbalance of one or more pairs, and this imbalance could cause some change in behaviour.

So far we have only briefly looked at a simple problem with one strand and the effects this could produce; we can now continue the process. Around the drawing of the heart we can add a few more 'problem' boxes with strands entering the heart in the same way. Very quickly there is a hopeless tangle. Not only are all the pairs of feelings involved but it is difficult to distinguish which strand belongs to which problem. Even if different colours are used for each strand, the resulting mess looks daunting to try to unravel. It always reminds me of going into a room in which a playful kitten has discovered a bag of wool! Where do you start?

SETTING THE SCENE

Anyone who has had experience with kittens, or even with just trying to unravel a tangled skein of wool, knows that two factors must prevail if the situation is to be saved and disaster averted—patience and keeping cool, calm and collected. A kitten caught in the act, or rather caught in the tangle, will respond to the person's tone and approach. The 'right' response will calm him down; the wrong response will send him off into a frenzy of effort to escape, resulting in a state worse than before.

If a kitten can show signs of guilt (some people would dispute this) because of its behaviour, and if its behaviour is made worse by being approached in a 'wrong' manner, how much more will a person, whose behaviour has resulted in a lowering of performance, react if approached in a similar 'wrong' way?

The manager who has a problem with one of his staff should decide whether the emphasis is to be on discipline or on counselling. I have indicated earlier that the two are not exclusively incompatible but unless you have a definite goal in mind you may find yourself vacillating between one and the other. If you are not sure of your goal (although it doesn't matter that you may not be sure how you are going to get there), your staff member will be thrown into confusion. If you decide that his misdemeanour cannot be overlooked, that is fine; you have decided on your goal: to discipline him. You may also feel, having disciplined him, that counselling is indicated. Whether this is possible in the same interview or subsequently, will depend on the nature of the problem, how you have dealt with the discipline aspect, whether or not it has been a formal or an informal disciplinary interview and the outcome.

Many people remember discipline as standing before the Commanding Officer with the Charge Sheet being read out by the R.S.M. where the outcome of 'guilty' is inevitable, with a subsequent punishment. The experience of others is of a lecture or a slanging match. Others, during discipline, have awakened memories of the parent/child or teacher/pupil experiences of discipline and the emotions attached to them.

Probably the most dispassionate of the examples given above, and therefore the one most likely to leave the way open for counselling, is the military procedure, where what takes place is 'by the book'. I suspect that managers who do end up arguing violently with the miscreant or lecturing him, have no book of rules to guide them; or if they have, they are unfamiliar with it. The soldier who has received the just punishment for his misdemeanour, as a rule, bears no malice towards the officer who has awarded the punishment. That is because personal feelings have not influenced the decision. The soldier has transgressed some law, or order, of which he had knowledge, or of which it was his duty to have knowledge.

I do not suggest that organisations should become para-military units, but more than a few leaves could be taken out of their books. If the manager has formulated rules of procedures which have been agreed and accepted by his organisation, any breech of these could be dealt with as dispassionately as in any military establishment. If the rules and procedures are just and fair, the person who violates them will know that discipline is merited. If the manager's discipline is inconsistent and harsh it will breed resentment. If his discipline is justly and consistently meted out, although the person may not *like* what has happened, he is more liable to respond to counselling.

Before any interview, but particularly where discipline is involved, make certain you possess all the facts and that you are familiar with them. Nothing is more off-putting than the interviewer who keeps referring to bits of paper for details which he might be expected to have known. It will help wherever there is the possibility of a discipline case, if everything which takes place is written down as soon as possible. A log kept in this way will ensure that you do have all the facts and there is then less possibility of dispute at a later stage. It is always sound policy to write to the person after a disciplinary interview stating the reason for the interview, the points discussed and the outcome. Again it must be emphasised that whatever you do must be in strict accordance with the established procedure.

The comments I have made about discipline may seem out of place in a book on counselling, and if we were considering therapeutic counselling they would be less appropriate. If, however, you agree with the basic premise of this book—that staff counselling arises primarily, but not exclusively, because of some performance problem—and if you also agree that some aspects of performance may require disciplinary action, then it is logical that sometimes counselling and discipline may overlap. What must be aimed at is a balance between the two. There are managers who always discipline and never counsel and there are those who have gone over-board on counselling and never discipline their staff. Neither the one nor the other, by itself, is sufficient. Counselling is a management tool and not a panacea. The manager who concentrates on the one and neglects the other could be accused of mismanagement.

If you have decided that counselling is called for, there are certain preliminary points which must be considered. You have to determine precisely *why* you are counselling, and this requires spending time thinking around the problem. You must also be in possession of the same facts as you would need in a disciplinary interview. This fact-finding exercise is very useful for it makes you stop and think. The conclusion you reach may be that some of the 'facts' turn out to be opinions, impressions and hearsay. Keep facts separate from opinions and feelings but do not disregard feelings; they may provide you with clues to important areas of exploration.

Where you conduct your interview and how the room is arranged is also important. Most managers are fully acquainted with the basics of interviewing: seating, arrangement of furniture, privacy and so on are all adequately dealt with in most management courses. Unfortunately you can have all the conditions 'right', be perfectly charming and achieve nothing. Perhaps the whole process needs to be examined.

THE SUMMONS

When you have gathered all your facts (I know this is not always possible—if for instance, someone knocks on your door, you can't very well say, "Oh, will you come back later, I must collect all my facts"), and you have decided when and where the interview is to be held, you and the other person must actually get together. Do you ask your secretary to arrange the interview? Do you write to him and ask him to come? Do you ring him up? Do you go round and see him and arrange a mutually convenient time?

If *you* are busy at something important and you receive a telephone message through the secretary or someone else to go and see the boss, what do you think your reaction might be? Can *you* drop what you are doing because someone else wants to see you? Would a better approach be (although it may be more time-consuming) to go to (say it were Tom) and say, "Tom, there is something I want to discuss with you. Could we arrange a suitable time, now or later today", and suggest a time? This will surely encourage active co-operation and not merely compliance.

I would like here to say a few words about the use of Christian names. Some people think that the use of Christian names indicates a cosy, friendly atmosphere, but does it? Conversely it is felt that the use of titles encourages respect. Both of these are myths which do not stand up to close examination. The fact that I constantly use a person's Christian name may not prevent me from sticking a knife in his back; the fact that you call your boss 'sir' is not a true indication that you respect him. There is more than one way of saying 'sir' to indicate true feelings!

The use of a person's Christian name indicates that you are on good terms, and it is often easier than Mr, Mrs or Miss. If one person addresses another by his Christian name, he is indicating equality, but if he does not expect that person to use *his* Christian name in return, he is creating distance and inequality. Inequality exists in this way between parents and their children, but the children in their turn use 'mother' and 'father' which reduces the inequality. This relationship is a special one.

In the teacher/pupil relationship there is again inequality where the teacher uses the pupil's Christian name (or surname) and the pupil uses 'Sir', Mrs or Miss.

In the working relationship the manager who uses Christian names but insists on people addressing him as 'Mr' (or never actually says not to) is creating inequality which has echoes of the master/servant relationship. If there is an age difference between him and his staff they could experience all the feelings of the parent or teacher relationships. If these were not happy, such feelings could create relationship difficulties between the manager and his staff.

You may ask what this has to do with counselling: I would refer you to the paragraph above where the manager approaches Tom to arrange a meeting. If Tom has not been in the habit of being addressed in this manner by the manager, what is he likely to feel? He could feel rather like the little boy who has been caught doing something naughty by his father who says, "Tom, come here; I'm not going to hit you", then with a smile still on his face proceeds to hit him. This incongruous behaviour is very often carried over into adult life and Tom could feel very suspicious of the sudden use of his Christian name. This could be a manoeuvre to reduce distance and make Tom feel more at ease—but the opposite effect is likely.

The staff member who initiates counselling usually needs help with some personal problem. The manager, on the other hand, is more likely to initiate counselling when there is a problem directly related to work. The staff member who requests the interview is already motivated to work towards a solution. The manager who has to deal with a work problem should bear in mind the point about resistance and must do everything possible not to induce or increase resistance.

In the case above, the manager gives Tom the option of 'now or later'; each has advantages for both of them. Can you think of some? If Tom says, 'later', this will give him time to get his defences together, if he knows the reason for the interview. If he does not know the reason and still says 'later', his level of anxiety is almost certain to reach a high peak by the appointed time. If the manager says, "Come now", Tom may feel trapped; anxiety and fear may create such a wall of resistance that the manager will have difficulty getting round, over or under. Nevertheless the manager must grasp the nettle and if he is sensitive to the fact that his approach may contribute to anxiety, he will also be sensitive enough to recognise its presence and deal with it.

If the staff member requests 'help', there is little preparation the manager can make. In any case, it would probably be more constructive, if time would allow, to see him without delay. Sometimes this is not possible; if this is the case, do tell him when you can see him. Some people use this as a deliberate ploy, either to gain time or (I suspect) hoping the problem will go away. If your reason for delay is genuine, it will be accepted; if it is not, the person will see through it and it will be just one more difficulty with which you will have to contend.

Some managers feel more competent to deal with work problems than with personal ones. If they initiate the interview they feel safe, certain that they can deal with it because it is 'work'; because they feel in control. If the staff member wants to discuss a personal problem, the manager has to leave the security of his work base and move out into the sphere of personal counselling.

ARE YOU SITTING COMFORTABLY?

An essay should have a beginning, a middle and an end; an interview should be similarly constructed: a great deal of thought and planning takes place before the essay is started. So far we have dealt exclusively with preparing for counselling and I hope you will agree that, just as in many other jobs, preparation is vital. Thoughtful preparation lays down sound foundations for constructive counselling.

We have looked at how the manager can prepare himself and also how he can prepare the staff member. The physical conditions—privacy, freedom from interruption and seating—all need looking at. Do make sure the chair you give Tom is comfortable, and try and arrange it so that the height of *your* chair does not mean that you look down on him. What do you do about the desk? Sitting behind a desk conveys a degree of formality; appropriate in a discipline interview but in counselling it creates a barrier by putting distance between counsellor and client. It is strange, but true, that emotional contact is made just that bit more difficult when there are physical barriers in the way: conversely emotional contact is easier when people are within touching distance. Personally I like the client's chair to be to one side of my desk and all I have to do is to turn my chair round and we are in face-to-face contact. Some people are able to arrange two easy chairs, right away from the desk; not everyone is so fortunately placed.

The time and place have been decided and Tom has now arrived. We have already discussed his possible feelings and it would be natural for him to anticipate the way the interview would go. He knows he has slipped up, probably feels guilty, angry with himself, depressed and possibly fears the worst.

THEN WE'LL BEGIN

Your opening words are important, but it is not always easy to get started. Some people evade the issue, possibly because they do not know how to deal with it; possibly because they feel sorry for the other person. They beat around the bush and in the process disturb a whole host of dormant feelings which fly around like frightened game birds. They talk about the weather, friends, hobbies, in fact anything but the real issue. If this approach is used, I can imagine Tom thinking "What's his game? I know I'm on the carpet, why doesn't he get on with it, it must be something bad and he can't deal with it." This attempt to put the person at ease is almost certain to heighten anxiety and frustration to such an extent that Tom's thoughts could become quite murderous.

Even though this may be a genuine attempt to put him at ease, it may also be due to uncertainty. You may not have thought the problem through, you may not have decided whether discipline or counselling is called for, or you may be unskilled in counselling. Uncertainty will be picked up by the other person for, like fear, or any other negative feeling, it is transmitted from one person to another, thus creating insecurity. To balance this, confidence and other positive feelings are just as easily transmitted, creating a sense of security. Man is still very primitive, at least at the emotional level, and insecurity arouses the instinct of flight or fight, whereas feeling secure is conducive to well-being and amity.

The client who comes for counsel must trust the counsellor if anything is to be achieved. If he is experiencing insecurity, as is highly probable because of his problem, his expectation is that counselling will somehow reduce it. If the counsellor also feels insecure, the client may pick it up without identifying its source, and this double portion of insecurity will undoubtedly lead to the feeling of flight or fight.

This flight/fight response places the client in an untenable position. He could walk out of the interview, but this is probably more than his job would be worth; if he reacts by fighting the manager, verbally if not physically, again his job could be jeopardised. What happens in this situation? Some do fight, others flee (the fight or flight may be physical or emotional so that although physically the client is still sitting there in reality his spirit has fled), and retreat into silence, afraid to say what they feel, afraid to trust their feelings.

The manager who has prepared himself well, has thought through the problem—in other words has done his homework—and has already established a satisfactory pre-counselling relationship, can feel confident that the foundations of that particular interview have been well and truly laid and this confidence will be transmitted to the counsellee.

The manager who feels confident to deal with the situation will not beat around the bush but will get straight to the point (an enquiry about his wife's health, or some other matter may be appropriate *if it is pertinent to the problem*). "Tom, I want to talk about the incident of the machine; tell me what happened" leaves Tom in no doubt what the issue is, and while he may not like talking about it, he is bound to feel a sense of relief that, at least, he is being given a hearing.

Very often the manager who is inexperienced in counselling will make sure that he puts his case forward first. Certainly he may have done his groundwork, collected all the facts and so on, and then as soon as possible he sails in with guns full blast. He amasses his 'evidence' then proceeds to list all the deficiencies, "You did this, and this, and this; and you said that, and that, and that; and I think, etc, etc." This barrage of defects and shortcomings will, by sheer weight, convince the counsellee of the case against him. This is unfair and demoralising and is certain to generate antagonism. Far better, as illustrated above, to let him have his say; by so doing you will permit many feelings to be expressed, and do remember that unexpressed negative feelings will get in the way of constructive counselling.

TIME TO GO HOME

Just as careful preparation for counselling is important so is the way the session is brought to a close. Whenever I speak to people about counselling, the question is invariably asked "How long should one session last?" If I throw the question back at them they produce various ideas and opinions. On more than one occasion the answer "As long as necessary" has been put forward. How long is that? One hour? two? a day? Such an answer, well-intentioned though it may be, does not display much insight into the counselling process.

I have yet to read any book on counselling where the author does not advise a time limit, and certainly during my professional training this aspect was always stressed. If professional counsellors feel it necessary to keep more or less to a fixed time, how much more should the manager follow their example?

Managers manage time, and if they do not organise it efficiently they could be accused of squandering a most precious resource. A reason why some managers do not counsel their staff may arise from the half-truth that counselling is time-consuming. I would suggest, however, that it is less time-consuming than the alternative. If counselling results in better working relationships or some improvement in performance it must be time well spent.

If the person who believes that the counselling session should take as long as necessary puts this into practice, I would suggest that he would very quickly realise that the rest of his work was being neglected. Quite apart from this is the emotional drain; counselling can be very exhausting. The knowledge that there is a time limit can be a positive safeguard for both manager and staff member.

Personally I like to keep any counselling session to about an hour although it may be less; beyond this time, efficiency begins to drop off rapidly. When I am seeing clients over several weeks they themselves quickly learn to draw the interview to a close. In staff counselling, however, you may see the person only once or twice (although as I said earlier, you may need to think of on-going counselling sometimes) so you may have to be more direct and tell him approximately how long the session will last, if for no other reason than that he may have to make arrangements for someone to cover for him. He may feel less anxious if he knows there is a time limit; if the problem is a personal one this knowledge may make him feel less guilty about using your time. It also gives a sense of urgency to the interview which can be positively helpful.

A useful guide (which should not be too rigidly adhered to) is to divide the allotted time into four equal parts. The first quarter would deal with a statement of the problem—an introduction: the next two quarters would explore the problem and work at possible solutions. The last quarter should be a drawing together, a restatement of what has taken place and a pointing to areas of growth or change.

This last point is often best dealt with by the client. Encourage him to tell you what he feels about the session, progress made, new developments and possible solutions. Far better this way than listening to you; if he hears himself say it, he will be more inclined to listen and believe!

How do you terminate the interview? "I see time is up" is usually sufficient except possibly to make arrangements for another session if necessary. Resist the temptation to pursue tantalising leads which frequently emerge just after you have said 'time'. This 'hand on the door' phenomenon is very common and is a manoeuvre (conscious or unconscious does not matter) to get more of your time. Either that, or he has introduced the new subject at this stage knowing that there will not be sufficient time to discuss it—he just wants you to know. If you have no time limit you are more likely to get new topics raised in this way. "Perhaps you can raise that again next time if you wish", or something like that, will let him see that you have heard but you are sticking to time. If you have apportioned your time in the interview in the manner suggested, you will have started to draw the threads together in such a way that he is prepared for the termination.

The timing of this summing up is important, especially if the interview has had its emotional moments. It is possible that at some stage he has become emotionally upset, more especially if the problem is a personal one. It would be very unwise to end on this note but if you have devoted the middle part of the interview to exploring the problem he will have sufficient time, in the drawing together phase, to adjust his emotions before facing the outside world.

People who have experienced an emotional release during a counselling interview may well discover what Sam did. He wrote:

"You remember that particular session, I think it was after we had been meeting about a month, when I was particularly upset. We had been talking about my father and how I had always regretted that we had never had a relationship where we could talk. You helped me to see lots of things about him and mother which I had missed. It was the realisation that now he was dead and the chance to get to know him was lost which broke me. I'm glad you didn't try to stop the flood gates; I had not wept like that for years.

When I left you (and thanks for the tea, it did help), I still felt tearful. Throughout that day, at odd moments, my eyes would fill with tears. I know people I met must have wondered what was wrong, and if they had asked me I would probably have burst into tears again. It was several days before I was back to my normal self."

Whatever the heightened emotion, every effort should be made to help him get back on an even keel before leaving your office.

POST–COUNSELLING

Sometimes a strange thing happens when counselling has taken place. The counsellor may be rejected by the client. The more intense the session (or sessions), the more of the problem which has been revealed, the greater the risk of rejection. As I see it there are four possible explanations.

One is that the client *does not feel better;* he has not been offered instant solutions, he has been made to work hard, his motives and behaviour have been questioned. To sum it up he feels let down. "If you had been any good you would have . . .", etc.

The second explanation is that he regrets having 'spilled the beans'. He may feel he has been manipulated, tricked into 'telling all', or at least more than he now wishes he had revealed.

A third is that having poured out his heart he feels he cannot look you in the face. You may know more about him than any other person, and he could not tolerate being reminded of this every time he meets you.

The last is that in fact what he told you was not true, or at least not the whole truth, and again he feels he cannot face you.

Rejection is of particular significance in the work environment where manager and staff member are in frequent contact. It may show itself in avoidance in normal social interchange, open hostility, or a refusal to accept further counselling.

If you, as manager, experience this rejection, to ignore it would be as difficult as it would be inadvisable. This type of behaviour clearly indicates further counselling, and you will need to demonstrate just how much you care. You may have to go out more than half way towards him and by your concern get behind the barrier which has been thrown up between you.

Sam at one stage rejected me. It was shortly after the incident related above. One day he did not turn up for his session and no message was received. I telephoned the following day and said "Sam, I wondered if everything was alright with you as you didn't turn up yesterday." He made some polite remark, apologised for not contacting me and said he would be along next week.

He did come, and after a few minutes said "Do you know why I didn't come last week? I felt that maybe we would go through all that again and I couldn't bear that. I don't think I would have come today if you hadn't taken the trouble to ring."

Some counsellors would disagree with my approach; they would feel it was putting pressure on Sam. What do you think and how would you deal with this situation at work?

SUMMARY

Before we start counselling it is essential to have some understanding of ourselves as well as other people. This understanding helps us to appreciate some of the feelings which clients may experience. In this chapter I have focussed on the heart as the seat of affections, to illustrate how positive and negative feelings balance each other. This balance is frequently disturbed by external and internal pressures and it is this state of emotional imbalance which brings the client and counsellor together. Imbalance may show itself in the way a staff member performs his duties.

Many managers never resolve the dilemma between discipline and counselling. Discipline and counselling, although quite different in outcome, have some areas of overlap. It is possible, if discipline is conducted in strict accordance with the rule book, to use this as a jumping-off point for counselling. Problems, we saw, could be simple—one-stranded; or complex—multi-stranded.

The interview was looked at in the following way:—

Preparation	— pre-counselling criteria; fact-gathering.
The summons	— how you get the person to the place at the required time.
The beginning	— don't 'waffle'—get to the point.
The middle	— whatever happened here? (see next chapter).
The end	— Draw the threads together. Does counselling ever end?
Post-counselling	— One of the dangers: how do you deal with it?

Question

How did you respond to the word 'summons' on page 86?
Did you feel this was peremptory, a command, an order?
If you felt this, think how the 'client' would feel when
'summoned'!

CHAPTER 5

Exploring the Problem

THE BIT IN THE MIDDLE

In the previous chapter we looked at how pre-counselling preparation can influence the way the interview commences. We also discussed how to apportion time so that the interview can be terminated so as to avoid leaving the client frustrated or emotionally vulnerable. We now consider the middle of the interview—half the allotted time—where the problem is explored and possible solutions examined.

I indicated at the beginning of Chapter 4 that problems could be classified as 'simple' or 'complex', depending on the number of strands or facets. It is also useful to divide problems into 'personal' and 'performance'. We all know people who are very difficult, who constantly irritate us, whose personalities are abrasive, who act on everyone like coarse sandpaper. It seems that everywhere they go they create tension, and generally working relationships are unhappy. You would probably be right in saying that such a person had a personal problem. The second category are those whose performance is causing concern.

This is an artificial distinction and in practice it would be very difficult to say that something was exclusively one or the other. But it should be possible to arrive at a conclusion that what causes concern is *basically* personal or performance. Please bear in mind that a problem in one area of life very often influences other areas.

The manager who has to counsel a person who, on the face of it, only has a performance problem may appear to have a simpler task than he who has to deal with a florid personal difficulty. The person who is an inveterate manipulator of people, and creates factions, is more difficult to counsel than someone like Sally (page 51) whose difficulty was localised to work. For this reason I always advise managers, when they are thinking round the problem, to put down these two headings, 'personal' and 'performance', then under each, write down all aspects of the problem. When this is done you will have a much clearer picture which may help you to see ways of resolving some of the difficulties. It may be that when you have made this two-sided list you end up with only one item under 'performance', in which case you would seem to have a personal problem to deal with. Under 'performance' you could also consider the following question: does the behaviour of the person in question create performance difficulties in other people? If the answer is 'yes', and even if you have not been able to isolate anything else, that is sufficient to make a start.

Tom's boss could demonstrate quite clearly where he had defaulted, so he would be on safe ground to start talking about performance. If Tom had approached him with, "Can I talk to you about a problem?" and had then proceeded to talk about his personal worries, again there would be no difficulty. But if *you* initiate the interview you would be on safer ground to start by talking about some aspect of performance than about something to do with personality or character.

100

Very probably it will emerge that the performance problem is only one issue; one strand of a complex problem. It is usually much less threatening to be tackled about something we *do* than about something we *are*; but can the two be separated? Exploration of what is wrong with work may reveal something about personality hitherto not recognised by either of you.

So far I have not expanded the theme of what one does with the strands of simple or complex problems. If you refer back to the illustration of the heart, you will see that problems disturb the emotional balance because they have become tangled up with the emotions. I said that a simple problem is relatively easy to deal with merely because there is less entanglement. One way to deal with the problem would be to try and unravel all the different strands simultaneously. Another would be to concentrate on one strand at a time. This, I feel, is the simpler method.

The reason I say this is that if one aspect of a complex problem can be even partially resolved, the resultant improvement in the emotional balance will make it easier to explore other areas. It is very probable that as one strand of the problem is extracted, others will show themselves.

When you are carrying out 'selective exploration' (one strand at a time) don't ignore other strands when they appear, but don't explore them at that stage. I inferred that some people deal with the total problem: non-selective exploration'. They explore one strand until another crosses its path, they then explore that one and finish up with a criss-cross of strands rather than a more or less linear pattern. The end result is no doubt the same, but I feel that selective exploration is more suitable for staff counselling because it is easier to control. If you select one performance strand and explore it with the counsellee, and if the result is a lowering of tension, you will both be encouraged to explore one of the other strands which emerged but which you chose to put on one side to be dealt with later.

I like to think of exploration as something exciting; one never knows what lies just around the corner but do bear in mind the points about exploration which were discussed in Chapter 2, the principal one being, never allow *your* excitement and eagerness to push the client faster than his emotional understanding will allow. Remember, you are an explorer and not a member of the national hunt, pursuing a fox with the aim of bringing back a trophy. The huntsman, chasing over the field at break-neck speed, could quite easily miss the cunning fox who has doubled back on his tracks and is leering at him from the undergrowth. The counsellor, making haste in the same way, could miss some important clues which could lead to new discoveries. Every activity has its optimum pace; anything faster results in reduced efficiency. In counselling, the pace is set by the client, not by the counsellor.

SIGNIFICANT AREAS FOR EXPLORATION

While it is true that every individual is unique, and this is what makes counselling so fascinating, there are certain basic areas which are common to everyone, although obviously there will be many different patterns. In a way it is like writing. There is one basic shape for the letter 'p' but think of the different forms it may take!

I have said more than once that seldom is the problem circumscribed or limited to one area. As we consider each area, please remember that what appears to be delineated, and neatly categorised, is only presented in this way to facilitate understanding.

Work

Because we are dealing primarily with counselling in the work situation I will take work as the first significant area to be explored. An important aspect is the attitude a person has towards work. Personally, I think of work as a relationship. If you think what you have read about relationships so far in this book, you will recall that one of the basic ingredients is give and take on both sides. Work forms a major part of one's day and accounts for a significant slice of one's life. Some people drag their feet through the working day, giving little and expecting much. The philosophy of others is just the opposite; they realise that if they are to gain something more than money, they must contribute something more than time. No relationship runs on perfectly oiled wheels at all times; even the most harmonious relationships pass through times of testing. Does the basic philosophy towards work of the person you are counselling have any bearing on his performance, if indeed performance is a problem?

Does the person himself realise his performance is causing concern? It is always useful (in fact, essential) to be able to demonstrate exactly how his performance is deficient and by what standards it is judged. Does he know the standard? What effect does his performance have on him? If he knows he is under performing, does he care? If he doesn't care, what does this do to him? If his pay packet depends on his performance, what effect does that have, and on whom? What reasons does he give for under performing? Ask yourself if he is 'moonlighting'? The person who tries to serve two masters may well end up not being able to serve either effectively.

Does his performance affect others at work? If so, how and whom? The answers to these questions should be made specific. If, for instance, he works as a member of a team, his underperformance is very likely to affect them in several ways. Sometimes overperformance by one person can create relationship difficulties as much as underperformance. He should be helped to see the consequences of his behaviour to himself and to others.

Is the total performance—output, working relationship, atmosphere—suffering through what he does? Can the department, organisation, stand the strain. Should they, even if they can?

You will see from this one section that we have already started to move out in an ever-widening circle, and the answers to one or more questions could suggest new avenues to explore.

Home

Most of us have somewhere we call 'home', where we go when our work is done. What do you know about the home of the person you are counselling? What does he think of home? Is it a haven or a burden, a place of rest and relaxation or a bedlam from which he escapes as often as possible? If he escapes, to where does he run?

Who is at home? Parents, wife, husband, children, flat-mate? What are his relationships with each one who is there? How much of his problems at work does he take home, and vice-versa?

Activities

Work takes up about one-third of the average person's day; sleep about one-third; what does he do for the remainder? Hobbies, interests, sports are all important indicators of the quality of life. Another important factor is religion; not so much that he goes to church or does not, but his attitude towards why he does or does not.

The different groups to which a person belongs is also significant. The values, beliefs and activities of one group may conflict with those of another, resulting in confusion and ambiguity. How does he deal with this conflict and does it influence his performance?

Relationships

In the section on work, I said that relationships in a group or department are likely to be adversely affected when one person's performance does not match up with what is expected of him. It also has to be borne in mind that even where performance is not the major issue, the person may have relationship difficulties with some member or all members of staff.

In trying to identify the areas of tension, ask yourself the following questions: with whom does he experience most difficulty; and a corollary of this: is there anyone with whom he does *not* experience difficulty? The answer to this two-part question can be very enlightening. Is the difficulty persistent or does it change? If it is not consistent, what factors influence it? The question 'with whom does he experience difficulty' should include sub-sections about the sex, age and personalities of the people and the type of jobs they do. For instance, he may experience no difficulty whatsoever with male staff but cannot tolerate young female staff, or vice-versa: he may work better with people older than himself, and so on.

Exploration of relationships at work would probably lead quite naturally to looking at other relationships: family (for example, spouse, children, parents or whoever his family is); friends (for example, what does he expect from friendship? what does he feel he gives to others?)

A study of relationships invariably touches on relationships in the past as well as in the present. Very often we react to people because of our experiences in the past. We cannot ignore these, and it is always useful to see how much the person is allowing them to interfere with the way he relates to people in the present.

This leads me to deal with the final section.

SIGNIFICANT PEOPLE

In the above sections we have already touched on several significant people, but it is useful to consider them separately. Just who the significant people are is something only the person himself can decide. A general question, "Who would you consider are the significant people in your life?" may baffle him for a few minutes; perhaps he has never thought of it in this way. Have you? At this stage it might help if you stop and consider that question. Jot down who they are, why they are significant, how long they have been significant to you and how you would describe your relationships with them. You can help your client by examining this question under the headings given above. You could also help him to look at significant people in his past to see how they influence the present.

THE INNER SELF

I have said that counselling is concerned as much with what the individual *is* as with what he *does.* So far we have concentrated mainly on exploring what he does—his behaviour.

In order to understand the person we need to recognise the feelings which activate his behaviour. Anger, fear, anxiety and depression (all negative); joy, happiness, tenderness (positive) to name but a few, all influence what happens within the emotional heart. What happens there influences the way he behaves towards the significant people in his life and in the areas described above.

THE PICTURE EMERGES

I do not suggest that you explore any one area 'ad nauseum', nor that areas are explored in any set order. Indeed it may be that you never have to give more than a gentle lead, a hint, a suggestion of what next to explore. "How do you get on with people away from work?", may show the person the way to go. Little by little the picture emerges of the person, how he relates to people, his behaviour and how it influences his work. This picture is as important for the client to see as for the counsellor. Perhaps he has never before been able to see himself in quite this way. If this is so, something of the skill of exploration which he has experienced will assuredly provide him with a foundation to continue the process long after formal counselling has ceased.

ANALYSE, DO NOT CRITICISE

I listened one day to a music critic comparing a number of records. There was no question about his competence or his appreciation of the finer points of musical composition and interpretation. *My* ears were unable to distinguish very much between the various performances, nor was my technical grasp sufficient to understand all he was saying. What he *did* say left me feeling slightly uneasy and dissatisfied. I pondered this for some time, unable to pin-point the reason for feeling as I did. Gradually it dawned; I was reacting to what is basically a negative approach. Newspaper critics very often delight in pulling to bits various performances in much the same way the music critic did. The essence of the critic's work is judgment based on specialised knowledge, and while it is undoubtedly true that a critic will often highlight good points as well as not-so-good, his judgment is based as much on taste and opinion as on fact.

Analysis obviously forms a substantial part of the critic's work, for indeed he has the ability to break down the performance into its various parts. Having broken something down in this way, he then appears to concentrate on the deficiencies. It is this essential difference which makes analysis appropriate and essential in counselling, but criticism inappropriate and out of place.

The process by which the counsellor analyses a problem is identical to that of the critic in that they both identify the individual component parts. The counsellor uses skill, knowledge and experience just as the critic does; the basic difference is that the counsellor *exercises* judgment but he does not *pass* judgment.

In one sense, both manager and critic follow more or less the same path, particularly in staff counselling where performance is in question. The critic judges performance; so does the manager. Where the paths are widely divergent, and where criticism is totally inappropriate, is when counselling is related more to personal problems than to performance.

The whole point about the function of analysis in counselling is to identify the various strands of the problem and by exploration to help the client to work towards a solution. Undue emphasis placed on the client's deficiencies, without due recognition of his strengths and contributions, will undermine his self-regard and make it more difficult for him to look at possible solutions in a positive way.

THE CASE OF TOM JENKINS

I want to bring this chapter to a close with the case study of Tom Jenkins whom you have already met. What I want to do is to highlight the various strands and show that what started out as a performance problem turned out to be very complex.

Part 3 will deal with a number of counselling interviews. The first four of these relate to Tom and show how the manager tried to help him unravel some of the strands.

As you read through the case you might find it useful to make notes of the type of questions you would want to ask Tom if you were the manager.

The Case

Tom is an employee in the laundry of the Loamshire Hospital which is situated some six miles from the town of Southdown. The hospital has been a significant employer in the locality for a number of years.

Tom, aged 27, has been employed there for three years; prior to that he had served in the Army. He is married with two children and they all live with Sheila's parents about a mile from the hospital.

He is employed on four automatic washing machines and is responsible for selecting the load (according to the type of article) and ensuring that the correct programme card is inserted. The whole laundry operates on a bonus payment system which is reduced when machines are left idle.

Part of Tom's job, when loading the machines, is to ensure that the loads are evenly distributed between the three cages of the one machine. He must also ensure that the cage door is secured; faulty securing will result in damage to the whole machine causing lost time and bonus. The laundry superintendent, Jean Rankin, telephoned the laundry manager to lodge a complaint about Tom. He had not fastened the cage door properly and as a result one of the machines was now out of commission.

The manager, Andrew Jones, had been appointed to the District only a month before (there were several hospitals in the District); before he saw Tom he did three things: read through Tom's personal record; visited the laundry to observe how everyone was working, including Tom; spent some time talking with Jean Rankin.

From the personal records he discovered that Tom had been to grammar school; there was no mention of educational or other qualification. He had served six years in an infantry regiment; there was no mention of rank. No incidents of disciplinary action had been recorded while he had been employed in the laundry.

While he was observing work in the laundry, Mr Jones noticed that Tom never seemed quite on top of the work; his machines never worked to full capacity; at least one of them was empty much longer than it should have been. He just gave the general impression of not coping. Mr Jones could detect a distinct 'atmosphere' in the laundry.

When he spoke to Jean Rankin he was told that over the past few months she had spoken to Tom about several things. His timekeeping was not all it might be, he was only a few minutes late most times but this meant that other people were held up. He was also absent rather a lot, not usually for more than a day. His wife would ring in and say he was not well; there was never anything specific. When she asked him he had replied "Nothing serious, just didn't feel up to the mark." He had been off with a certificate for one week with a strained back. Sometimes he would disappear from the laundry—to get cigarettes from the hospital shop—but he would never ask. When he was tackled about this he would say "It was only a minute." She added that rumour had it that he was in debt.

Mr Jones went round the laundry again with Jean Rankin. He wanted to speak to Tom about the latest incident but felt that to take him away at that time would only make matters worse; work was already beginning to pile up due to the damaged machine which the engineers were working on. He also felt he wanted to give Tom some say in when it would be convenient. "Tom, there is something I want to discuss with you. When can you come?" Tom looked at Jean Rankin as if for guidance, but she just shrugged her shoulders. "I suppose you would want to see me at the end of the shift but I've got to go (pause) . . . to (pause) . . . the doctor. Could I come tomorrow?" Mr Jones felt a prick of annoyance but trying to hide it said "It will have to be late tomorrow afternoon, I have a meeting in the morning."

EXERCISE

1. Make a list of all the factors you can identify as being potential strands to be explored.
2. At this stage who would you classify as 'significant people' in Tom's life?
3. What significant areas do you think you would want to explore?
4. Are there any points about the management process you are not happy with? If so what would you do?

SUMMARY

Exploration of problems can be dealt with under the headings of personal and performance; in reality there is a great deal of overlap. I have suggested that selective exploration is more suited to staff counselling than non-selective, because it deals with one strand of the problem at a time.

It is useful, when counselling, to make a note of the significant people and significant areas mentioned by the client. From your study of the case you should be able to make your own list of these and compare the two. Significant omissions by the client can then be picked up and thrown open for exploration. Exploration should provide the staff member with a clearer picture of himself in relation to significant areas and people. Exploration is facilitated if it is based on analysis and not on criticism, except possibly in the area of performance. If analysis is carried out with understanding of the person, criticism will be superfluous.

The Action

CHAPTER 6

Interviews
and Case Studies

ANSWERS TO QUESTIONS

At the end of the previous chapter I posed four questions. I wonder if my answers match yours?

1. Strands

1.1	Performance	— definite and demonstrable
1.2	Punctuality	— definite and demonstrable
1.3	Absence	— definite; possible link with health
1.4	Health	— possible; not convincing at this stage
1.5	Relationships at work	— possible because of performance
1.6	Debts	— possible; rumour
1.7	Housing	— possible; in-laws

2. Significant people

2.1	Jean Rankin	— superintendent; known by Mr Jones
2.2	Workmates	— known by Mr Jones
2.3	Sheila	— wife; not known by Mr Jones
2.4	Parents-in-law	— not known by Mr Jones
2.5	Children	— not known by Mr Jones
2.6	Tom's parents	— not known by Mr Jones

3. Significant areas
3.1 School
3.2 Army
3.3 Relationships as in 1.5
3.4 Activities and interests
3.5 Attitudes, with particular reference to work

4. Management process
4.1 Had Tom received adequate training?
4.2 Why had nothing been done about his unpunctuality and absence?
4.3 Why had Jean Rankin not complained before? Had her complaints not been listened to?

THE CASE OF TOM JENKINS

INTERVIEW 1

You will see that already you have started to make some assessment of Tom based on what you know. Mr Jones had done what groundwork was possible; he had not jumped in but had used his own methods to get his facts and impressions. We left Tom having made an arrangement to come to see him at the end of the shift the following day.

Tom did not appear at the appointed time and Mr Jones walked into the laundry room to find out why. He looked for Jean Rankin who seemed surprised that he should be enquiring for Tom, who apparently had not turned in that day; there was no message. "Do you want to see him particularly?", she said. Mr Jones reminded her that he had made an appointment in her presence the day before. She looked uncomfortable and mumbled something about not listening to other people's conversations. Mr Jones asked her to make sure that Tom came to see him at the same time the following day. Mr Jones made a note of events in Tom's file. A few minutes after the end of the shift the following day Tom knocked at Mr Jones' door.

T   1   *You want to see me, Mr Jones?*

Mr   1   *Yes, Tom, come in, sit down.* (Mr Jones looked at Tom across his desk and noted that he looked pale with dark shadows under his eyes) *Tom, I want to talk about the incident of the machine; tell me what happened.*

T   2   *Ah, well, it's difficult.* (Long pause) *Have you spoken to Jean about it?*

Mr   2   *Is that important?*

T   3   *Yes.*

Mr   3   *Tell me how it is important.*

T   4   *Well, she would probably say it was my fault even if it wasn't. She doesn't like me and she'll go out of her way to get me the sack.*

Mr	4	Do you think you could keep to the point and tell me about the machine.
T	5	I knew you wouldn't listen, you've probably made up your mind; perhaps I'd better leave anyway.
Mr	5	Is that going to achieve anything?
T	6	It would get me out of your hair.
Mr	6	(after a pause) We don't seem to have got off to a good start. I want to know from you about the machine, but it's obvious that you are angry about something. Do you want to talk about it?
T	7	I suppose I am angry, nothing to do with you though. I don't think I fit into this place at all. I've been here three years since I left the Army. This was the only work I could get so I had to take it. Some of the things I don't like doing and I'm slow. It's all rush: sort the stuff, weigh it, take out the washed stuff throw in the dirty and all the time there's Jean peering over my shoulder making sure the cage door is shut properly. It gets me down.
Mr	7	You feel you are not quick enough, is that it?
T	8	That's right. You must have noticed the great pile of dirty stuff waiting to be done. The other chaps get theirs done.
Mr	8	Yes, I did notice. Is it always like that?
T	9	Most of the time. The others work like clockwork.
Mr	9	M-hm (pause).
T	10	I don't get on very well with Jean, or any of the others. I feel I'm the odd one out.
Mr	10	Why is that?
T	11	They know I've had a better education than they have; I even talk better. It could be something to do with Sheila's parents. Anyway we don't hit it off too well.
Mr	11	Has it anything to do with your work, do you think?
T	12	I suppose it could be that; I don't do as many loads as the others.
Mr	12	M-hm (pause).
T	13	She can't blame me for the machine though. I know you don't believe me, (said with anger).

Mr 13 *You are pretty steamed up about the machine, aren't you?*

T 14 *Well, that's why you want to see me, isn't it? Why don't you come straight out with it?*

Mr 14 (Becoming slightly exasperated) *Hold it Tom; my first words were "Tell me about the machine", but you blew your top about Jean. I want to get to the bottom of it. I'm new here and naturally I want to get the laundry running the way I want. I would like you to help me by being straight with me. Don't beat around the bush. I may not like what you tell me, but for goodness sake let's get on with it, shall we? You could start by telling me what you mean when you say you couldn't be blamed for the machine.*

T 15 (Long pause, fiddling with his fingers) *My goodness, you sounded just like my old C.O. when I was on the carpet.*

Mr 15 *M-hm.*

T 16 (Another pause—deep breath) *Alex* (one of the other machinists) *did it* (said in a rush).

Mr 16 *Is that so?*

T 17 *That sounded sarcastic; I said you wouldn't believe me.*

Mr 17 *I'm sorry Tom, it wasn't meant to sound like that. I was surprised, I think. It's your machine; why did Alex have anything to do with it?*

T 18 (Hesitating) *I know it's against the rules, but most of the others help each other out when they can and . . .*

Mr 18 *Let me get the details straight. Are you saying that Alex helped you out; was that because you were behind?*

T 19 *Correct.*

Mr 19 *And Alex loaded the machine and fastened the cage door; did he switch on the machine?*

T 20 *Yes, I suppose he did.*

Mr 20 *Why do you suppose?*

T 21 *Ah, well, I . . . I* (pause) *. . . wasn't actually there at the time.*

117

Mr 21 *You mean you were attending to one of the other machines, is that it?*

T 22 *No, not exactly* (long pause). *I . . . I had just nipped out to the shop for some tobacco you see I . . .*

Mr 22 *Is it any wonder you get behind and can you expect . . .*

T 23 *O.K., O.K. put me in the wrong again. Everybody does it. Jean knows all about it and provided we get the job done she doesn't mind.*

Mr 23 *So when you came back you found the machine broken, is that it? This can't have improved things between you and Alex or the others. Their bonus has been affected and you should have asked Jean if you could leave the laundry . . .*

T 24 *She doesn't order me around, you know.*

Mr 24 *I'm not talking about ordering; I'm talking about cooperating with each other to get the job done, but I'm getting the distinct impression that this does not always happen.*

T 25 *I suppose you blame me for that?*

Mr 25 *Oh dear, Tom, you're very touchy, aren't you. Are you often like that?*

T 26 *Well I don't like being put in the wrong.*

Mr 26 *Have I actually blamed you for what happened?*

T 27 (Grudgingly) *Well not exactly, but it sounded a bit like it.*

Mr 27 *Do you admit that you were partly responsible?*

T 28 *No I don't. It's not my fault that there was a backlog of work from the previous day and when . . .*

Mr 28 *Let me get it straight. Tuesday you were off with your back, the accident happened on Wednesday; what happened yesterday?*

T 29 *Oh goodness, was that the day I was supposed to see you? I forgot.*

Mr 29 *You forgot your appointment, is that it? but you didn't turn in either. I went to look for you.*

T 30 *No, I didn't turn in. I guess I was too upset by what happened on Wednesday. Didn't you get my message? Sheila saw Jean Rankin at the bus stop and told her. Mind you it's not surprising she didn't pass it on.*

Mr 30 *What do you mean?*

T 31 *Well, she is ancient, isn't she? She should have retired years ago. She never remembers anything and she's as deaf as a post, especially if her hearing-aid battery is running down. Mind you she does lip-read fairly well.*

Mr 31 *Well, thank you for sending a message to say you wouldn't be in yesterday. It might be better another time if you ring in to the general office. I wonder if you can see what I was getting at earlier about relationships between you and the others?*

T 32 *I suppose so, but I wish Alex hadn't fouled the machine up and landed me in the cart.*

Mr 32 *Really Tom, this points to something much larger— the way you all get along with each other in the laundry. You've said yourself things are not all that bright and I asked you if you thought it was anything to do with the way you work. Do you think we might talk about that, unless you've had enough for today?*

T 33 (looking at the clock) *No, I've nothing to rush home for today. I . . . I* (pause, as he seemed to be searching for the right words) *. . . don't go a lot on this relationship business—I assume that's what you mean?*

Mr 33 *Yes Tom, that's what I mean, but tell me why you think relationships at work are not important.*

T 34 *Either people like each other and get on, or they don't.*

Mr 34 *Do you think there is anything you could do which would help the relationships between you and the others?*

T 35 *There you go again, it's all my fault* (silence).

Mr 35 *Sorry; let me put it another way. Do you think anything could be done which would improve the relationships between you and them?*

T 36 (thinking for a minute) *I like Alex, in spite of what he's done; not much between the ears, but he's fair and a good worker. I'll give him that, and he doesn't get huffy. I suppose if I pulled my weight a bit more it would help, but as I said I just don't think I'll ever be able to work like he does.*

119

Mr 36 *That's good Tom, that's positive thinking. Anything else?*

T 37 *No, not really.*

Mr 37 *What about time off?*

T 38 *I'm only off when I'm ill; you can't hold that against me, can you?*

Mr 38 *I wonder how the others look at it? How do you think Jean feels?*

T 39 *I thought she'd come into it soon. I suppose she thinks I'm swinging the lead; does she?*

Mr 39 *I don't know, I've never asked her. But I would ask you to put yourself in my shoes. I need reliable people here regularly, otherwise it means less turnover and lost bonus for all of you. Do you think there could be some reason why you need to have days off?*

T 40 *Well, of course, I do have a bad back, a disc or something and that worries me quite a lot.*

Mr 40 *In what way?*

T 41 *I wonder how long I'll be able to carry on doing this job and if I can't do this what else can I do?*

Mr 41 *What does your doctor think about it?*

T 42 (with a great deal of hesitation) *It's all a long story and as time is getting on I think I'll leave it, if you don't mind.*

Mr 42 *We didn't get off to a very good start, did we Tom? I think I trod on a number of your toes. I'm sorry about that. You said you were worried and I wonder if you would like to come for another chat?*

T 43 (after a pause) *Thank you Mr Jones, yes, I think I would. Mind you, I'm not an easy person, I know that, so you'll have your hands full. But perhaps we can hit it off. Can I come the same time next week?*

Mr 43 (looking at his diary) *I can manage that, for about an hour before I have to rush off to a meeting. Is that all right?*

T 44 *Thank you, I'll be there.*

Warning

There is always the danger in giving verbatim accounts that readers will be tempted to model their own interviews on the words rather than on the underlying techniques and concepts.

Having delivered this warning, the reader should analyse each response carefully and any comments which are made. A careful analysis of the actual spoken words and the responses made by both persons will undoubtedly enhance counselling skills.

HOW TO ANALYSE AN INTERVIEW

Some type of evaluation or analysis is essential following any counselling session; only in this way is continual progress ensured.

To help you analyse this, and other counselling interviews (I would suggest that this system and format could be used with profit after any interview) you might consider the following outline. You may have to hazard a guess at some of the questions, for one person can never *fully* understand the feelings of another. A fairly accurate guide to the feelings in this interview with Tom would be how you yourself felt as you read it through.

The questions are phrased as if *you* were conducting the interview. Only minor adjustments are necessary to fit the interview between Mr Jones and Tom.

1. *What was happening within me?*
   Relaxed, friendly, anxious, quiet, talkative, afraid tense, defensive, indifferent.

2. *What was happening within the counsellee?*
   This may be difficult for Mr Jones to establish, but it is an essential part of the post-interview analysis. If Mr Jones can try to understand what was happening within Tom, he will possibly get some clues to his behaviour.
   Questions as in 1.

3. *What was happening between me and the counsellee?*
    Participation, involvement/non-involvement, listening/talking; argument, persuasion, feeling versus intellect, reassurance versus exploration, tolerance, achievement of insight.

4. *Was the following behaviour exhibited?*
    Tension-release, support, caring, aggression, hostility, manipulation, rejection.

5. *Did you identify any specific examples of non-verbal communication?*
    This is difficult in a written interview but what non-verbal communication do you think there may have been? Some has been included.
    Body contact, proximity and position, gestures, facial expression.
    Eyes—contact, signalling.
    Hands and feet; legs and arms; breathing.

6. *Atmosphere*
    Formal/informal, competition/cooperation, hostile/supportive, inhibited/permissive, harmonious/destructive.

Here are a few more questions you should ask yourself about your interview technique.

1. *Listening*
1.1 Who did the most talking—the counsellee or me?
1.2 Did I make sure the counsellee said what he wanted to say?
1.3 Are there any clues I missed?

2. *Confrontation*
2.1 How well did I deal with confrontation?
2.2 Was I able to talk freely about performance difficulties?
2.3 Was I able to talk freely about relationship difficulties?

3. *Conflict*
3.1 Did I create hostility or aggression?
3.2 How did I deal with aggression?

4.   *Exploration*
4.1   What was my goal? Has it been achieved or partially achieved?
4.2   What strands have emerged which may be explored? What are they?
4.3   Which significant people have been identified so far?
4.4   What significant areas have emerged? Which have been explored?

ANALYSIS OF INTERVIEW 1

Questions

1.   Looking at the questions on page 110 and the answers on page 114 how many have been touched on in this interview?
2.   What is your general feeling about the quality of the interview?
3.   What do you think Mr Jones' goal was and what did he achieve?

I now want to analyse this first interview. As you will have gathered there are a number of different interviews between Mr Jones and Tom, and each one will be analysed.

It is useful to analyse any counselling interview under the headings 'problem' and 'process'. 'Process' would include approach, techniques, atmosphere—in fact what happens between counsellor and client. Under 'problem' you would include all the details of the problem which emerge, significant people and areas, and so on.

In addition to dealing with Tom is there anyone else at work with whom Mr Jones will have to deal?

Mr   1 In view of the seriousness of the case this is a benign opening. He is observant of Tom's appearance. He uses his desk, I think, to indicate that this is something more than a cosy chat. He obviously believes in getting straight to the point but does not accuse Tom.

T	2	*Tom obviously doesn't know quite what to do, and tries to involve Jean to turn the attention away from himself. He does not succeed but nevertheless what he says is useful information which Mr Jones will store away for some future occasion.*
Mr	2	*This is an example of a 'closed question'—one which can be answered with a 'yes' or 'no'—Mr Jones turns it quite well in the next response.*
Mr & T	4 5	*Tom does not like being nailed down and attacks Mr Jones quite strongly. What he says in this response and T 4 would suggest that he feels others are against him.*
Mr	6	*Mr Jones does not attempt to defend himself—which would have been a natural reaction. He allows Tom opportunity to vent his aggression, his negative feelings. The choice is Tom's—to talk about it or not.*
T	7	*Tom says a great deal here. He is really apologising, in an oblique way. He wants Mr Jones to know that although his anger is directed at him he is not the cause of it. This is not always easy to accept, is it? It is easier to accept if we have done something to cause the anger, if somehow it is justified. It is always useful to try to determine if the anger is arising as a reaction to something external or whether it arises from within the person without due cause.*

Some people need only a very small external stimulus for them to react angrily; others require much stronger stimuli. Tom's anger, at this stage, probably arose from a mixture of frustration and guilt, although later we shall see that there are other factors.

There is, however, another aspect of anger which is that Tom could have been responding to Mr Jones' approach. People who are *very* understanding can provoke certain people to react in the way Tom did.

Question

Why doesn't Tom fit into the ethos of the laundry? Think of his background, or what you know of it; his temperament and attitudes and his basic approach to work.

Mr 7 Mr Jones is no fool; he knows what Tom is talking about but wants to hear him say it. On the other hand, Tom knows that Mr Jones must have seen that he did not compare favourably with the others.

Mr 8 Mr Jones does not compare Tom with the others directly. Had he said "You're obviously not as good as Alex," for instance, this could have increased Tom's anger which at this stage is showing signs of abating.

Mr 9 When in doubt say nowt! Mr Jones probably feels that Tom is beginning to talk positively about himself and does not want to stop the flow. He may also feel that he doesn't want to give direction to the interview at this stage.

T 10 It is interesting that here Tom decides not to continue talking about his performance but returns to the theme of not fitting in relationships.

Mr 10 Mr Jones could have been tempted to offer verbal reassurances at this stage in an attempt to try to get Tom on to his side.

T 11 What effect do you feel Tom's attitude would have on his relationships? Mr Jones operates 'selective exploration' very well. He did not allow himself to be drawn away by the intriguing reference to Sheila's parents. He tries to get Tom to make the link between his attitude towards people and the way they react towards him.

T 12 Tom seems unable to make the link and sees only the performance problem.

Mr 12 I can well imagine Mr Jones thinking "Where do I go from here?"

T 13 I was puzzled by this remark and it is only when you refer back to Mr 11 that it seems to make sense. Although he did not verbalise the link between his attitudes and relationships he may have done so emotionally and realised his deficiency.

Mr 13 Mr Jones lets Tom see that he recognises his feelings and again focusses on the machine.

T   14   *A possibly explanation for his reacting in this way is that he has been meandering in (for him) the strange world of relationships; what he has seen has frightened him.*

Mr 14   *Mr Jones has been superbly patient until now; many of us, I feel, would have reached this stage of exasperation long before this. It is interesting that he responds in this way when his skill in interviewing is attacked. Tom's "come straight out with it" may mean "Show me your real feelings". He seems to have difficulty coping with someone as understanding and patient as Mr Jones who may have instinctively felt this. He makes an appeal to Tom to help him. You will notice that he does not leave Tom floundering but gives him direction by referring back to T 13.*

T   15   *An attempt by Tom to ease the tension.*

T   17   *Tom really does have self-doubts. What questions does that raise in your mind with reference to past relationships, particularly parental?*

Mr 17   *He bridges that awkward moment nicely.*

T   18   *In the whole of this section [T18—27] there is a gradual build-up of tension as Mr Jones applies pressure on Tom to get down to the real reason for the interview—the broken machine. Mr Jones shows that he is listening—really listening—by picking up the word 'suppose' in T 20. This puts Tom on a spot and he feels trapped; this is expressed quite clearly in T 23. His behaviour reverts to that of an earlier stage in the interview. Guilt? Mr Jones' response in Mr 23 sounds a bit like a lecture; perhaps Tom didn't need reminding that the bonus would be affected; perhaps he had heard it loud and clear from just about everyone in the laundry. In Mr 24 Mr Jones sounds more than a bit exasperated. It has been difficult for him; Tom will not even admit that he is partially responsible.*

126

Mr 28 *Tries to get back on safe ground—what actually happened. Did you wonder how long it would be before he got round to why Tom did not come to see him as arranged? What do you think Tom's reaction would have been if the interview had started with "Where did you get to on Thursday"?*

T 30 *What does Tom's 'too upset' suggest to you? He gets another dig at Jean.*

Mr 31 *Mr Jones probably recognises that he will have to deal with Jean at some stage; puts the focus back on Tom.*

T 32 *Tom appears to be moving slowly towards being able to look at himself, although in T 33 he confirms the fact that relationships are not his forte.*

T 35 *Tom certainly puts Mr Jones through it. He is right though; the implication is that Tom should do something. How different it looks reworded in Mr 35. (I can imagine Mr Jones rephrasing this with a wry grin on his face!)*

T 36 *Mr Jones ignores Tom's condescending attitude and builds upon the little bit of ground gained in the admission that he does not pull his weight. I wonder if he could have made just a little bit more of this? If he had asked a related question, like "Do you mean you feel you don't pull your weight?" it might have encouraged Tom to explore a little more how he actually did feel. As it is he seems to come back to the attack—"What about time off?". This puts Tom back on the defensive.*

T 39 *I wonder if Jean, or any of the others, have accused him of 'lead swinging'?*

T 42 *Tom appears to shy away from this subject, perhaps Mr Jones should have left it at T 37 or again pursued the subject of how Tom feels about being accused of swinging the lead. It looks as if he is trying to cram too much into one interview without really developing one theme. It could be that his own feelings have been trampled on to the extent that his equilibrium has been disturbed. I feel that in attempting to deal with too many strands of the problem he has caused*

127

confusion in his own mind and not allowed Tom to settle his emotions. It does appear that Tom has worries about his health.

Mr 42 *Mr Jones brings the interview to a close very positively, taking the blame but offering what help he can give.*

T 43 *Tom reveals a bit more—'not an easy person'—but it looks as if he is prepared to trust Mr Jones.*

Notes by Mr Jones after the interview

What a session! I wondered what I had let myself in for; felt I was trying to grasp hold of an angry wasp. Wish I hadn't lost my temper; console myself with the thought that he probably needed it.

A very unhappy, angry and frustrated young man with a great chip on his shoulder. I don't know if I can cope with him. Might need help from someone.

Pointers for the future

1. Jean Rankin—must talk to her.
2. Must explore his Army career.
3. How did he get taken on in the laundry in the first place?
4. Seems a bit of a misfit here, a bit B.B.C. for this crowd.
5. What was the reference to Sheila's parents?
6. Health—funny how he sheered off that—wrong timing? Enough for one day?

These notes show a depth of analytical thought and a willingness to examine his own performance. He may well discover that subsequent interviews present as many difficulties!

INTERVIEW 2

Pre-interview notes

1. Learned from Jean Rankin that the previous manager had been persuaded by the Hospital Administrator

(who was a personal friend of Tom's father) to find Tom a job when he left the Army. Jean didn't know the ins and outs of it all but it had created a great deal of ill-will at the time.

When asked about Tom's absences and time off, Jean sniffed and said, "I might as well have saved my breath. I spoke to Alan, your predecessor, who ignored it. 'Give him another chance,' he would say; favouritism, that's what it was. He'll never make a laundry-worker, the toffee-nosed grammar twit. He's not worth spending time on."

Gave me the impression that I was wasting my time. Am I?

2. Now I've arranged to see him, what on earth am I going to talk about? What should my aim be? I don't think he'll open up very much about relationships and he was chary about his health. I wonder if he would talk about the Army; would it help if I tell him I was in the Army? I wonder why he didn't get rank in six years? What went wrong with his education?

3. Can I justify the time spent? Is Tom going to benefit? Is the laundry going to benefit? Am I? If (and am I being too optimistic?) I spend time with him and he works better, is absent less, what will this do for general working atmosphere? Tom will benefit financially and the rest of the staff will work better—this must be profit. How do I benefit? Reputation for good staff relations; good turnover? I want to help him; what does this do for me? Makes me feel good, I suppose.

A few minutes after the laundry closed, Tom knocked at the door, Mr Jones got up from behind his desk, pulled his chair forward and invited Tom to take a seat. Tom picked up his chair and moved it slightly further away from Mr Jones. This puzzled Mr Jones.

Mr 1 *Hello Tom, I'm glad you could make it on time; as I told you I have to be away in about an hour and . . .*

T 1 *If you can't spare the time it doesn't matter.*

Mr 2 *Did I give the impression I didn't want to see you?*

T	2	Well I did wonder why you were going out of your way; what can you get out of it?
Mr	3	Do you want me to be frank with you, Tom?
T	3	Yes, please.
Mr	4	I don't like to think of my staff being unhappy, and you strike me as being not very happy; if there is anything I can do, that's what I'm here for. I was thinking about our last talk and wondered if you would mind telling me how it is you came to work here when you left the Army?
T	4	That's easy. You know what the job situation was like three years ago; when they threw ... when I left the Army I came back to live here; there was nowhere else to go. This job was going and I took it. (Mr Jones noted the change from 'they threw' to 'I left' but did not comment on it.)
Mr	5	How long did you serve?
T	5	Eight years, all told. I joined as a boy soldier at sixteen.
Mr	6	Tell me about it.
T	6	Nothing much really; saw a bit of the world, had a bit of fun here and there, bit of a drag in the end, though.
Mr	7	You decided you'd had enough, did you?
T	7	Wasn't quite what I thought it would be. Stupid bunch. Some of them were O.K. but some of them, especially one Corporal in boy's service, a right pig he was.
Mr	8	Did you get promotion?
T	8	Ha, Ha, that's a laugh, promotion, me? never on your life. I kicked from the day I joined till the day I left.
Mr	9	Sounds as if you had a pretty miserable time.
T	9	I gave them a miserable time, serves them right, rotten bunch of hypocrites. Promise you the world; "the world is your oyster" they said, and what do you get? pig swill and Blanco.
Mr	10	You sound bitter about it all, why did you stick it for eight years?
T	10	The money was good and I thought I'd learn a trade— all those promises in boy's service. I stuck that for

two years and at the end of it what did I get—foot-slogging with a lot of half-educated dim-wits. All they did was teach me to drive.

Mr 11 Tom, why did you leave school at 16; did you take 'O' levels?

T 11 Now don't you start; I had enough with my old man when he was alive, never forgave me for letting the side down. I can hear him now going on and on, "All our family have gone to the grammar school and have all done well, we want to be proud of you too." What a load of rubbish! Who's really interested in bits of paper anyway? I'd had enough of school. I suppose I am the black sheep. The only child, and what have I got to be proud of?

Mr 12 Do you feel you've let the side down?

T 12 No I don't. I've let myself down, I suppose. I could have done better at school and I could have made something of the Army if I'd really put my back into it.

Mr 13 What stopped you?

T 13 No real interest.

Mr 14 Did you have any ambition?

T 14 I didn't want to go to grammar school for a start. Most of my friends went to sec. modern and I wanted to go with them. I had to travel about six miles to school. I hated it from the first day to the last. The only thing I liked was art. I would have liked to study art.

Mr 15 That's interesting. I go to art classes every week and if . . .

T 15 Oh, I can't be bothered with that now, and its O.K. for you, you've made it, you're successful; look at me, 27 and still labouring.

Mr 16 Would you like to do anything different?

T 16 Naturally, but what could I do?

Mr 17 Let me ask another question, Tom. Have you done anything about trying to change things, like going to evening classes or doing a correspondence course to get some qualifications?

T 17 *What good would that do? They tried that in the Army but I wouldn't wear it. I had to take the Army exams in boy's service; kid's stuff, but G.C.E.'s, no fear.*

Mr 18 *If you don't want to take any education qualifications what else do you think you might do?*

T 18 *Well I am pretty good at drawing and I like carving but I couldn't make a living at that, could I?*

Mr 19 *Maybe not, but often hobbies can develop. Do you still do carvings?*

T 19 *Yes, in the evenings, when the work on the farm is done.*

Mr 20 *Do you live on a farm?*

T 20 (A trace of life on his face) *Yes, Sheila's parents have the Firs, a small dairy farm, and I help most days after work and at the weekends. We share the farmhouse.*

Mr 21 *You like the farm don't you? I can tell that. What do you like most about it?*

T 21 (Without hesitation) *Working with Bess, the horse. She's great. You know, I swear she understands every word I say. She'll be in the field near the road and when she hears me whistling, she'll gallop up to meet me. She's a lovely old thing, we're great friends* (pause for breath).

Mr 22 *You obviously like animals.*

T 22 *You can say that again. I wanted to join the Veterinary Corps but they wouldn't have me.*

Mr 23 *Why was that?*

T 23 *Said I couldn't show stickability, it's quite a long hard course.*

Mr 24 *How did you feel about that?*

T 24 *Boiling; "the lousy sods", I thought. It was just after I left boy's service. I picked up a magazine of the RAVC, until then I hadn't given it a thought. My application for a transfer was turned down. My C.O. laughed in my face. I nearly hit him.*

Mr 25 *Did you feel he might be right about stickability?*

T 25 *If you had said that last week I think I would have wanted to hit you, but somehow today is different.*

Mr 26 *M-hm.*

T 26 *Somehow I think you really care about me. I can't think of anybody who's spent as much time with me as you have, except in the Army when I was in trouble.* (As he said this he moved forward in his chair.)

Mr 27 *Thank you Tom. I'm glad you feel like that for that's how I feel too; that we're on a different wavelength from last week. Tell me why you think they said you couldn't stick anything.*

T 27 *The Selection Officer, just before I went into man's service, asked me what career I wanted and I just didn't know. He turned up all sorts of things, most of them so many 'O' levels, even 'A' levels. I knew I couldn't make it. He said then if only I could stick at something I might make something of my life. He wasn't very cheerful; said if I didn't stick at something I would be a drifter, end up as a Private after 20 years or as a labourer. He's right there, isn't he? His prediction came true.*

Mr 28 *Tom, I'm not quite sure how to put this but inside me I'm feeling pretty miserable and I think I'm picking this up from you; is that right?*

T 28 (Looking very uncomfortable) *You're spot on. Can I stop calling you Mr Jones?*

Mr 29 *Call me Andy, most people do.*

T 29 *Thanks, that makes me feel better, puts us on equal terms. I suppose I am miserable but it's never been different, at least not for years. I've made a proper mess of my life, so far* (angrily). *It's all my parents' fault.*

Mr 30 *How's that, Tom?*

T 30 (Long pause, obviously struggling with something very painful.) *Oh it doesn't matter, it's all in the past and I don't see how talking can help.*

Mr 31 (Moving forward and reaching his hand out towards Tom as if to touch him) *Try it.*

T 31 (Another long pause—got up and stood with his back to Andy, looking out of the window.) *I've never told a living soul this, not even Sheila. I'm not my father's son. I'm someone else's and I don't know who.* (He came and sat down again, his eyes filled with tears and he was very pale.) *A bastard, that's what I am, Andy. All right, in law I'm not, but that's what I am, a bastard, bastard, bastard. God what a mess. You know how I found out? When I was fifteen, mother and the old man were having one of their endless rows one night. I was in the attic doing some experiment, my workshop was up there; I think they had forgotten me. I heard the old man shout at her. "I suppose you've got another fancy man and then I'll have to take his child as mine, just like I did Tom." I couldn't hear any more, the door was slammed. I . . .*

Mr 32 *You mean to say that you've kept this to yourself all these years, you poor chap.*

T 32 *For God's sake Andy, don't pity me. I couldn't stand it. I haven't cried for years but if you keep looking at me like that I swear I'll blab like a child.*

Mr 33 *I suppose . . . I . . . (pause) . . . was thinking of my own lad and how close we are; he's sixteen. I felt so angry at your father just then for making you so miserable all these years. How did you cope with it?*

T 33 *I just shut myself off. I used to go to bed, put my head under the sheets and swear myself to sleep. That's why my schoolwork went to pieces. I hated him so much I just had to get away. I hardly ever went home on leave. Funny thing, I never blamed mother. Do you know, when he died I laughed. I thought, right, now you'll get your reward. What an awful thing to do.*

Mr 34 *Do you see what your bitterness is doing to you?*

T 34 *I know what it has done but how do I get rid of it?*

Mr 35 *Well, quite honestly Tom, this is away outside my scope. Would you go to someone else who is more experienced in this?*

T 35 *No, definitely not Andy. I feel I couldn't start all over again. I feel you have got through to me and I want to keep it that way.*

Mr 36 *I just don't know whether I can, Tom.*

T   36   Well, *perhaps I'll just call it a day* (got up to leave).

Mr 37   Wait Tom, *don't go like that. I feel so darned help-less. Sit down, please. Give me a minute to think about it.*

T   37   O.K. Andy. (pause).

Mr 38   *I think you'll probably agree that I'm getting out of my depth and if you won't go to anyone else would you let me seek help?*

T   38   *What do you mean?*

Mr 39   *I have a friend, Dennis, a Probation Officer; if I went to talk to him he would probably be able to give me some advice.*

T   39   *You mean you'll tell him all I've told you?*

Mr 40   *If that's all right with you?*

T   40   *Not my name, though.*

Mr 41   *No, that won't be necessary. I'll just say a friend of mine has this problem.*

T   41   *Thanks Andy, that sounds fine; when will I see you again?*

Mr 42   *I'm on holiday next week Tom, so this will give me a chance to see Dennis and I'll see you the same time two weeks today, if that's O.K.?*

T   42   *Thanks again Andy, see you then. Have a nice holiday. Don't do anything I wouldn't do.* (He picked up the chair, replaced it against the wall, and as he went down the path Andy heard him whistling a tune to himself.)

NOTES ON INTERVIEW 2

Never felt so helpless in my life; couldn't think clearly; wanted desperately to weep. Glad I persuaded him not to leave, I would have felt really bad. He did seem happier when he left. What would I have done if he had started to cry? Can I help him to get through this? How is he coping away from me? Even if I can help him, what will happen in his work? What's he going to do with his life? Right now I feel I can't carry the responsibility. I might make a hopeless mess of it and then what would happen? Funny how he started using my Christian name: that made me feel pleased; why, I wonder?

Andy rang Dennis and they arranged to meet. Dennis asked him to write down as much as he could remember of the two interviews and to bring the notes with him.

THE MENTOR INTERVIEW

When they met, Dennis read through Andy's notes.

D 1 *How do you feel I can help, Andy?* (This is a fairly innocuous opening which allows the person to choose his own direction.)

A 1 *I didn't feel too bad after the first interview; felt I coped with that well enough, but when he told me about his father, I just started to boil and yet at the same time I wanted to cry, felt so helpless. I haven't got the skill to deal with this sort of problem, have I?*

D 2 *Are you saying that I have?* (In an oblique way Dennis is saying "Are you implying you would like me to take over?" If he had said this directly, the discussion could have centred around whether or not this were possible.)

A 2 *Well, you are a professional; you know I'm interested in counselling and I went to that series of lectures you organised, but I've never come against anything like this.*

D 3 *And you need help, that's it, isn't it?* (It may seem that Dennis is labouring the point but in reality he is getting Andy to take a good look at why he is there.)

A 3 *Right.*

D 4 *Andy, as far as I can see, it's not so much how you tackled it that's worrying you but something within you which may need looking at.*

A 4 *Do you mean I've got some hang-up, some blind spot?*

D 5 *Something like that. As I read your notes, and from what you said, you appear to cope fairly well, in fact, very well with Tom's anger and I think you did a good job to get him to agree to come back a second time. If you coped so well then, why do you think the second interview proved so difficult?* (Dennis could have entered into a debate about blind spots, an intellectual discussion on psychology, but he decides to get Andy thinking. He gives a professional opinion about Andy's performance and is quite specific about the areas where he feels he has achieved some success, but uses this to point to the real problem.)

A 5 *It started off O.K., I felt we were getting somewhere. I thought we were on to something important when he was talking about the Army. I thought he was going to say "They threw me out", then changed his mind. I shouldn't be surprised if I am right. I had wondered if I should tell him I had been in the Army, but I thought better of it.*

D 6 *What made you change your mind?*

A 6 *Well, of course I was commissioned and this would have rubbed his nose in it and he could have resented me.*

D 7 *That's good thinking. You obviously have got on to his wavelength. It's like that sometimes, difficult at first then it just happens. When did you feel you were on the same wavelength?*

A 7 (After several moments pause) *Difficult to say exactly, I knew I was getting somewhere when he moved forward in his chair (T 26, p. 133) I felt he wanted to get nearer to me. And then of course it really clicked when he wanted to call me Andy.*

D 8 *How did you feel at that?* (You notice that Dennis is all the time seeking clarification, not only for what happened—(the process)—but how he felt.)

A 8 *A bit choked really; does that sound silly to you?* (The fear that feelings are silly and that they may be rejected.)

D 9 *Do you feel it's silly?* (Putting it back at Andy, making him stand on what he feels.)

A 9 *No, I don't. I'm glad it happened that way. Until then it was 'him' and 'me'; after that it was 'us'. I suppose it was because I felt I had established a relationship.*

D 10 *You had?*

A 10 *Sorry, I should have said 'we'. I implied that it was what I had done, didn't I?*

D 11 (Smiling) *You're getting it, Andy, keep at it* (Encouragement). *Tell me how you felt when he told you about his parents.* (You will notice how Dennis is leading Andy gently on. When he demonstrates that he is achieving some understanding he goes a little further, never too much, never too quickly. Not only is he going at Andy's pace but he is keeping to the sequence of events. In this way he is allowing Andy to re-experience the feelings he had during the interview.)

A 11 *When he got up I though he was leaving. He stood for quite a few minutes, looking out of the window. I felt very lonely at that stage; isolated, an on-looker. I sensed he was struggling with something. Strange, Dennis, I'm not particularly religious yet I found myself praying "Oh God, help him; help me." He looked so forlorn, all hunched up. I didn't really see him as a man, he was just a little boy. But at the same time I felt lonely. I wanted someone to hold me and comfort me. My feelings were all jumbled up; I wanted to cry with him. He sensed this, I'm pretty sure, yet at the same time I was angry. I felt it was happening to me, why was that?*

D 12 *As I see it, Andy, there are two possible points. How you saw him and how you responded to his feelings; you were obviously picking up his feelings without him saying anything. Do you think he could have been looking out of the window or possibly looking in, or do you . . .* (Andy, interrupts Dennis who has obviously opened an emotional window in Andy's mind.)

A 12 (Excitedly) *Stop, Dennis, you've broken something.*

Looking in, that's it. I was looking in and in a way
seeing myself. I lived in a town and I would often
stop and look in windows where there were lots of
children . . . (pause)

D 13 *M-hm.*

A 13 (Andy rose and went to the window, looked out for
a little while, came and sat down with his head in
his hands. Dennis waited, sensing that just as Andy
had waited for Tom to struggle through, he too
would have to wait. He reached out and put his hand
on Andy's shoulder. This seemed to release something
and Andy started to weep. During his weeping he
said, "Hold me, Dennis, I'm frightened." Dennis put
his arms around him and held him tight without saying
anything. When his sobbing had stopped he said . . .

D 14 *That was quite an experience, Andy.*

A 14 *I don't need to apologise, I don't want to. I know*
you understand, thank you for your strength.

D 15 *Yes, Andy, I've been through it, but what broke you?*
(Dennis could have related his own experience which
would have taken the focus off Andy. This may have
put a brake on. Sometimes this is helpful if you feel
the other person is allowing the cork to come out of
the bottle too quickly.)

A 15 *It was the window. I looked and saw myself; as a*
little boy I used to think "Wouldn't it be fun to have
lots of brothers and sisters," but somehow I just
knew that would never be. I knew from quite a
young age (although I can't actually remember being
told) *that I had been adopted. Mum and dad made no*
secret of it. I was a few days old; they couldn't have
any of their own. There was a time, when I was about
eighteen, that I used to wonder who my real parents
were. I made some half-hearted attempts to find out
but didn't pursue it. Funny thing, it was my dad I
wanted to know about. I talked to dad about it and
that was the only time I ever saw him cry; he felt
sorry for me.

Something I wasn't able to talk about was my
awful loneliness; I think I must have made a nuisance

139

of myself for I became quite possessive of my friends.
I wanted them exclusively to myself, didn't want to
share them. It wasn't until I went into the Army that
I was able to relate to groups of people.

D 16 Do you still feel lonely at times? (Bringing it from
the past to the present.)

A 16 *Right, and just now I really was frightened. I'm glad*
you were there. Do you think that's how Tom felt?

D 17 *I guess he felt something like that. Do you see why*
you reacted like you did with Tom? (Gently leading
him on.)

A 17 *Rather like two lonely souls together, I suppose;*
perhaps he too was frightened by what he was feeling.

D 18 *Is it just loneliness?* (Dennis probably left this deliberately open-ended to see if Andy would make the
link between loneliness and fear which could account
for Tom's anger.)

A 18 *Is it something to do with my own uncertainty about*
my parentage, not really knowing; not having any
roots? You can probably go back several generations.
I feel as if I had just 'happened'.

D 19 *You describe Tom as an angry, bitter young man;*
does this account for his loneliness do you think?
(Dennis seems to have moved the focus from Andy
to Tom; why?)

A 19 *Yes it might do. People get fed up after a time with*
his attitude, the way he talks about people—'thick',
'nothing between the ears' and so on, no wonder they
give up.

D 20 M-hm.

A 20 *You're trying to get me to think of something else, I*
can tell, just the way you say 'm-hm' (smiling). *Do*
you think there might be more than just loneliness
with me, that I might be angry or bitter? (Is he
making the link Dennis was hoping for?) *I don't go*
around like Tom, do I? You can't mean that?

D 21 *Perhaps not exactly similar. Do you never become*
angry?

A 21 *You're infuriating, Dennis; of course I do, but it*
tends to be with myself and not with other people.

I get quite angry whenever I see cruelty, or unkind-
ness, especially to children. I think I was more angry
when a boy. I used to fly into tantrums and stamp
my feet. Dad used to laugh at me and clutch me in a
bear-hug. I would struggle to get free, when I couldn't
I would end up laughing; I always felt safe in his
arms. Like I did just now. He was lovely; still is; they
both are. I've been lucky, Dennis, I have so much.
No, I don't think I'm an angry person. If I had been,
I think I would not have been able to handle Tom's
anger like that. What I couldn't handle was his
pathos. That's because it stirred up my own feelings
so much.

D 22 *I'm sure you're right, Andy. I'm also sure that during*
the next few days things will keep popping up from
the past; some you will like, others may be painful.
Enjoy the pleasant ones, but don't turn your back
on the painful or disturbing ones. Look them squarely
in the face; explore them; accept them, they are a
part of you. When you have looked at them in this
way, their sting will gradually go, like a scar which
fades with the years. Does that make sense?

A 22 *I understand what you are saying but it's too fresh*
for me to say 'yes' emotionally. All I know is that
right now I feel empty and yet contented. Is that
what they call catharsis?

D 23 *Yes, but it doesn't always happen like that and one*
of the dangers is that some people will try and
manufacture it and can't understand why it back-
fires. You, Andy, needed to be held, but some
people are so repelled by physical contact that
even as much as they are crying out 'comfort me',
cannot accept it. We all have to work through
catharsis in our own way. You may never experience
anything quite like this again. Don't try, but don't
stop it happening either. I'm sure you will look at
Tom through different eyes. Perhaps you can stand
at the window with him and look at what he is look-
ing at without feeling all churned up inside.

A 23 *I'll let you know how it goes. I could do with a cup*
of tea!

COMMENTS ON THE MENTOR INTERVIEW

This session between Dennis and Andy has been introduced to show the value of this type of relationship. This was a fairly dramatic example, probably because it was a strong emotional reason which prompted Andy to seek help from Dennis. Dennis was quick to realise that in this particular instance it was not the process of counselling—what Andy did—on which he should concentrate but on Andy himself. This also illustrates how vulnerable we make ourselves when counselling others. We can never know, when a counselling session starts, just how it will progress or how it will end. But it is also true that only as we make ourselves vulnerable can we achieve increasing understanding of ourselves and other people.

It is doubtful if Andy could have achieved insight into this part of himself if he had not persisted with Tom. It was him, and his problem which triggered this off in Andy—one of the grey areas.

ANALYSIS OF INTERVIEW 2

Did you notice how Andy moved his chair from behind the desk, indicating that the discipline aspect has been dealt with? (You may feel that it had not been adequately dealt with; was it?) Did you also notice how Tom moved *his* chair away? What interpretation did *you* put on that?

They almost started off on the wrong footing. Perhaps Andy should have realised how sensitive Tom is and shouldn't have referred to time. Tom, in fact goes on to express something of the guilt some people have of using other people's time in this way.

Andy does not apologise but is honest and in [4] gets Tom talking about something which is fairly safe. Tom's rebellious attitude starts to show through in [8]. Not only that, but his obvious misery comes over to Andy who picks it up in [9].

Tom has given vent to some of his feelings about the Army but there is some ambiguity; in [11] Andy seems to have the point about 'O' levels cleared up. This remark unearths a

142

great deal more of the problem and especially Tom's bitterness and resentment, and yet there seems to be a hint of regret, a tinge of guilt in the last sentence of [11]. In [12] is he also showing signs of regret?

Andy makes an attempt in [15] to get Tom interested in art, without success. The same thing applies to education. If he were going to offer to take Tom to art classes it was probably too soon: do you think he was going to suggest that? It was probably too soon to hope that Tom would think seriously about education. There is a great deal of negative feeling to be got rid of before positive action can be considered. What does emerge, however, is his interest in the farm and his love of Bess. Is there a connection between what he has told Andy and his unpunctuality and possibly his absences?

Andy risks a rebuff by his question in [25]; if it had been mis-timed how do you think he would have dealt with it? Tom's remark in [25] seems to be the turning point; he can now take this remark from Andy because he recognises that he cares. I feel that Andy has made real emotional contact with him. Note how Tom moves forward in his chair, (watch for non-verbal cues).

Andy responds, [27], in a natural way, giving positive feedback. You notice he refers back to what 'they' said about stickability. By doing this he is removing it from himself—*he* is not saying that Tom does not have stickability. It is possible that by referring back to the Army he might have caused Tom to become angry again as the bitterness came to the surface. He might have done better to have said something like, "What is it that's brought about the change?" As it is, Tom does not become angry, he seems to be honest and faces reality.

Andy was no doubt able to pick up Tom's feelings because they were now on the same wavelength (empathy). The change from 'Mr Jones' to 'Andy' seems right, just here. If Andy had done this, Tom could have been suspicious. I don't think this came easy to Tom and it is quite a step forward in going out to meet Andy.

Tom does not deny his misery and by admitting that he is miserable he allows himself to start looking at the reason.

Why do you think he stood with his back to Andy? In a way it is like closing your eyes; either to stop *you* seeing, or to stop other people seeing your eyes and what is going on in them. This is borne out by his remark to Andy in [32]. The depth of feeling is emphasised by the repetition of 'bastard'. If this is how he has regarded himself, one can well imagine how he must feel when people use this word in general conversation.

Andy is deeply moved by this recital and cannot help comparing this with the relationship he has with *his* son. He recognises he is getting out of his depth and wisely admits it. It is right that Andy tells Tom what is involved and Tom retains some control—his name. I like the way Andy refers to Tom as 'my friend' [41].

Tom's closing remark indicates a definite change in mood, something has been accomplished. He probably feels that a burden has started to lift, indicated by the whistling.

POST–INTERVIEW NOTES

After Andy had seen Dennis and before he was due to see Tom next, he had a word with Jean, who told him that Tom had been absent only one day in almost three weeks. She seemed pleased. Andy asked if Tom had contacted anyone. Jean said he had rung through and explained that one of the cows had been ill and he had been up all night and couldn't come in. Andy asked Jean about the previous occasion when Sheila had given her a message. She admitted that she had forgotten and apologised; "Sorry about that, I know my memory's not what it was, not much longer till I retire, hope I can last that long." Andy realised there was little point in trying to put pressure on Jean and was thankful he had made arrangements for Tom to ring in. He did wonder how many other messages were not being passed on!

INTERVIEW 3

Pre-interview notes

If I was concerned before the last interview, I'm doubly so now. How will Tom respond? Will he regret having told me? Will he be his old, angry self? I hope not; if he is, I feel it will be my fault. Glad I had Dennis' support. Dennis was right, things have kept popping through. I used to love to read fairy stories about children who were orphans and were found by some rich couple. Never liked reading about those who were left orphans, like after an accident. Realised that even now I don't like watching television programmes about orphans or illegitimate children. I think now that I realise all this, I shall be able to deal with these feelings better. I never thought I would be thankful to go through such an experience. I wonder how Tom coped with it? Mustn't rush him, he'll tell me in his own time.

Andy heard Tom's whistle before he knocked on the door. When he came in they spontaneously shook hands in greeting. Andy hadn't realised how large and strong Toms' hands were.

T 1 (Smiling and relaxed) *Hello Andy, good to see you, hope you had a good holiday; go somewhere exciting?*

A 1 *Didn't go anywhere, did the garden, a bit of decorating and so on, had a good time with my friend Dennis and now I feel ready for work again. How have you been since last time?*

T 2 *You can see a difference, can't you Andy?*

A 2 *I see you are not miserable.*

T 3 *Right, when I left last time I felt very strange. You know I was talking about being a bastard, well I realised, as I was cycling home, that's what I have been, a proper bastard to everyone . . .*

A 3 *Tom, a thought's just struck me; how do you get on with women?*

T 4 *That's just it, I get on great, no bother. I think I could have worked with women. Even in the Army I had no bother with them, enjoyed their company, never played loose with them, mind you. Never*

145

wanted to get them in the family way, never went with married women either. I'd seen the misery this could cause.

A 4 *So you weren't a bastard to everyone, were you?*

T 5 *No, you're right, only men. I must have been taking it out on all men because of my old man.*

A 5 *Was he all bad?*

T 6 *You're getting at me Andy, but I don't mind. You can say what you like, I can take it now. No he wasn't all bad. In fact when I look back today I must admit that he gave me what I needed; nothing frivolous or extravagant, toys were usually educational, that sort of thing. I did have a dog, though; Skipper was his name; a collie. That's another thing I'd forgotten until just now. He died, old age, just about the time . . . just about the time I heard dad say that.*

A 6 *I expect you missed him?*

T 7 *Yes, of course, but not as much as you would imagine. I think I was too taken up with the other business.*

A 7 *You know, Tom, you called him 'dad' just now?*

T 8 *(Surprised) You're right, why was that I wonder? I've called him 'old man' for years, never referred to him as anything else if I could help it: 'dad' seemed to stick in my throat.*

A 8 *Perhaps you don't hate him quite so much?*

T 9 *Oh, I wouldn't say that (pause).*

A 9 *I just wondered if by hating him less it would allow you to be more free with other men.*

T 10 *Good point, you might be right there. In fact, looking back I would say you are right. You, for one. I like you and I think I'm getting on better with the other men in the laundry. Perhaps all this is working. Do you know, I've only had one day off and that's because we'd trouble with one of the cows. We were up all night, but we pulled her through; a good night's work. Sheila's dad was pleased with me. I get on fine with him. In fact he offered to take me into the farm full-time.*

A 10 *Will you?*

146

T 11 *Would you mind if I did, after all the time you've spent helping me?*

A 11 *I'm pleased for you Tom, if that's what you want to do. The time has not been wasted. I don't quite know what has happened within you but something has obviously changed. I also know that I have gained something very precious and wouldn't have missed our time together.*

T 12 *You make me feel choked, Andy. You're a real friend, I hope I'll always have you to turn to.*

A 12 *Of course. Can you tell me what has happened?*

T 13 *I'll try. I went home that afternoon whistling, the first time for years I'd done that. I kept asking myself why I was happy. I almost missed my misery! Sheila noticed something was different but I couldn't talk about it. I wanted time to think. I still haven't told her about . . . you know, but I will one day when the time is right.* (pause). (Andy waited.)

T 13 *It happened the night I looked after the cow. I'd persuaded the others to get some sleep and I stayed with Bella, trying to make her comfortable, giving her medicine and drinks regularly. It must have been about 3 in the morning and I think I was half asleep when I heard someone say, "Love, don't hate." I thought it was Sheila's dad but there wasn't anyone there. Just then Bella opened her eyes and I swear there was love in them. I knew she was better. I thought a lot that night, or what was left of it. You spoke of bitterness but I realised that it was in fact hate, and I know that at times this could have driven me to murder. There are very few people I can call my friends and there are even fewer I can honestly say I love. You have been showing me something of what love and friendship are, in the way you care. I may not be able to show people that I care for them in the way you do, but I am going to start. If I don't, I'm sure I'll do something drastic.*

A 13 *That sounds quite a revelation.*

A 14 *It is, and another thing I realised was that, as much as I hate other people, that much more do I hate*

147

myself. If this is right, then all the time, I'm punishing myself for something my parents did before I was born. I can't go through life like that. I've got to do something constructive and useful.

A 14 *Do you have anything in mind?*

T 15 *I said that Sheila's dad had asked me to go full-time and I think I will, but I don't feel quite ready yet. Can we go back to something we were speaking about earlier? I had plenty of time to think and I realised why I felt happier. Because I had shared my secret with you I felt it was no longer as dreadful as it had been. I think too that getting rid of that has allowed me to start caring. I know Jean was surprised when I brought some eggs for her the other day. I find I can chat to her and the others now. They still call me 'butter-fingers' but I can take it now. I talked to them about going on the farm full-time, they thought it was a good idea.*

A 15 *Do you think you could spend the rest of your life farming?*

T 16 *I think so; it's not an easy life but I do enjoy it and the farm will be Sheila's one day. She knows as much about it as her dad does. I think we can make a reasonable living from it.*

A 16 *You said you didn't feel quite ready; why was that?*

T 17 *I don't want to leave here until I've put things right. That may sound daft, and I'm not quite sure what I do mean. I've run away so much in my life, this time I want to walk away, knowing that I leave behind me friends and not enemies.*

A 17 *You have been doing a lot of thinking. Will you tell me when you feel ready to go?*

T 18 *You'll be the first to know, Andy. You gave me hope as well as friendship and I want to keep it that way. I now realise what I've missed for the past twelve years. People could never get near me. I was afraid if they did, one of us would get hurt and I didn't want it to be me. I still have a lot of learning to do.*

A 18 *Do you feel you need to come again or do you feel you're getting to grips with your problem by yourself?*

T 19 *I don't think I need to come again but if I feel things are getting on top of me, I know you'll be here.* Tom rose, replaced his chair, stood looking out of the window for a second, then turned round with a smile on his face and said, *"What did you see, Andy? I know what I saw. Cheerio for now, and thanks."*

POST-INTERVIEW NOTES

Glad for Tom he has achieved some degree of self-realisation. Feel slightly sad that our sessions are over; perhaps this is because I've gained so much from them. Hope his venture works out.

ANALYSIS OF INTERVIEW 3

Even before Tom arrived there were clues as to his mood. There are some people who hum and whistle in order to keep up, or lift up, their spirits. It is not always possible, therefore, to deduce accurately which it is. Their gesture of greeting seems natural here: it is two weeks since they met and such a lot has happened within both of them—they have met again after their respective voyages of discovery.

Andy gives Tom the opportunity to ask about his visit to Dennis but he chooses to answer the question rather than respond to the invitation to ask about Dennis. It would have been quite natural for Andy to want to share this, but either Tom does not attach much importance to it or he is absorbed with his own experience.

In [3], Tom makes quite a significant emotional move when he stops personalising the word 'bastard'. The fact that he can now refer figuratively to himself as a 'proper bastard' indicates that he has started to accept himself. The process of acceptance may not yet be complete but I feel it is well under way. The sting seems to have gone out of it.

His use of 'everyone' prompts Andy to ask about women who, so far, have not figured significantly. One of the points which Andy may be trying to get Tom to look at is that it is not 'women' but 'one woman'—his mother. In interview 2 [33, page 134] he says he never blamed her, but Andy may have felt that this attitude was unrealistic and that he was trying to deny his real feelings towards her. It is true that at this stage Tom's relationships with women have not been explored. If he had experienced difficulty in this area it would probably have emerged before this. What Andy does is to show Tom that his 'everybody' is not quite accurate—only men. We do not know how he relates to children. His attitude towards women is summed up in the last sentence of [4].

Andy is now in a position to encourage Tom to take another look at his father through eyes not bedimmed by hatred. Although he will not admit to hating him less, he does in fact demonstrate that this is so, by the way he now relates to the others.

Andy leaves Tom in no doubt that *he* has received as much as Tom from the relationship. The fact that he will be there if needed, helps Tom to recount what had happened.

Tom's phrase "I almost missed my misery" speaks volumes. He had lived this way for so long, his misery had become a habit and happiness was virtually a stranger.

His graphic description [T 13] shows how well Andy had prepared the ground. This account emphasises the oft-repeated fact that frequently more takes place *after* the counselling session than during it. Andy touched upon quite a number of important areas and subjects, and, as it were, helped Tom to loosen the cork of the bottle. In this particular instance the cork 'popped' in the early hours of the morning. His tenderness towards the sick cow was probably the channel through which realisation came that love is essential to life.

It must have been quite frightening for him to realise that the feelings he had been jealously harbouring could have driven him to murder. He also realised that in the process of hating he is the one, above all others, who suffers most.

He transferred his new-found affection to Andy, the person who, in his eyes, has made all this possible by his caring attitude. Some managers would find this profession of affection difficult to deal with. Andy doesn't attempt to comment on it, feeling, no doubt, that he has, by his actions, said all there is to say.

Andy in [15] selects Tom's future as the point to be explored without referring again to Tom's past. He obviously feels that Tom has gained enough insight to be able to pursue some of these avenues on his own. Tom, however, has not finished and wants to show Andy that his caring has taken a practical outlet directed at Jean.

Did you wonder why he did not bring Andy some eggs? There are at least two possible explanations. He gave them to Jean as a practical demonstration of a change in their relationship, to prove his intentions. He did not do this with Andy; their relationship was already established. Giving eggs to Andy could have been interpreted (by Andy or Tom) as some sort of payment, and this might have interfered with the relationship. Can you think of any other reason?

Andy makes a rather abrupt return to the question of farming [15], when Tom was beginning to feel his way to talk about relationships. Perhaps he feels he should be drawing the threads of the interview together but wants to test the reality of Tom's idea. The fact that his mates thought it a good idea could be viewed with caution—they may be glad to be rid of him; perhaps someone else wants the job! Perhaps the change in their attitude is related to the prospect of Tom's departure in the near future.

Tom shows a surprising stickability [17]. The cynic might suspect that the time wasn't quite right for many other reasons, but what he says makes a great deal of sense. Far better to leave friends behind than enemies.

Andy, once more, tries to draw the session to a close [17], but again Tom insists on saying his piece. He is reassuring Andy, I think, that his efforts have not been wasted. He says in a few words what many people feel about keeping people at a distance because they don't want to hurt or be hurt. Tom probably recognised his potential to hurt people and so avoided them. Is he also acknowledging the part Andy played in this change? By allowing Andy near he can now move out towards other people.

SUMMARY OF TOM JENKINS

At the beginning of Part 3 certain factors were identified as possible areas for exploration. Health, although it was touched on, did not appear to be as significant as the pre-counselling facts led us to suspect. The subject of debts never emerged and there was a logical explanation as to why Tom and Sheila were living with her parents.

Of the significant people in his life, only the relationship with his father was explored at depth. His mother hardly emerged as a significant character at all. The feelings centred around Tom's father, and if Andy had attempted to explore the relationship with his mother it is doubtful if he would have succeeded. He was too caught up in the trap of his negative feelings to look at other relationships. If the situation had not been resolved it would have been necessary to examine his feelings towards his mother more fully. But it is possible that Andy would not have felt competent to do this even with the help of Dennis. Why? Relate this to his own background.

There are many unanswered questions about his relationships with other people, although we can assume they were reasonable. If this had been a problem it would have shown itself somehow.

The exploration of the significant areas was quite thorough and rewarding, although again there are some unanswered questions. We still do not know, for instance, how much trouble he got himself into in the Army or if he was 'thrown out'.

I feel this case illustrates the strength of the counselling relationship; Tom felt he was cared for, and without being poetic and sentimental, he saw and experienced love in action.

Andy, through Dennis, achieved insight which illustrates something of the value of the mentor relationship. As it turned out, Andy had already achieved a great deal before his session with Dennis and had he continued with Tom beyond Session 3 he would not have been so emotionally over-involved and he would thus have been able to deal more constructively with Tom's emotions.

Question

What did *you* see as you looked in or out of *your* window?

POSTSCRIPT

About two months after these interviews, Tom came to see Andy to tell him he wanted to leave. He and Sheila had gone into the whole question thoroughly with her parents and felt it was the right course to take.

Tom still had miserable moments, but he felt they were getting less frequent and were not so intense. He had been reading a book on 'positive thinking' which had helped. His relationships at work had improved and when he actually left, his mates subscribed to a leaving present.

He had not yet been able to tell Sheila. When he could think about his parents (and note it was now 'parents' and not just 'father') without feeling angry, that would be the time to tell her.

EXERCISE

Refer back to the questions on pages 110 and 114 and try to relate these to the three interviews between Tom and Andy and between Andy and Dennis. This is not an easy exercise; it is time-consuming and may require several readings of the interview before you get the hang of it. Good luck!

THE CASE OF SHEILA ARMSTRONG

INTRODUCTION

The previous case study was what I would describe as a 'complex problem' because of the number of different strands. Andy Jones worked within the limits of his experience. The problem he dealt with may not be typical of staff counselling but it proved a useful vehicle for a study of many important points of counselling process, as well as highlighting how behaviour is influenced by emotions hidden deep within the personality.

The case of Sheila Armstrong is different. First, it is only one interview. Secondly, the setting is different. Mrs Quinn, because of the role of Occupational Health in industry and in this instance, the N.H.S., is more akin to the professional counsellor. She has no disciplinary function and because of this some of her remarks, if they came from a manager, would very possibly be interpreted as disciplinary.

The third point in which it is different is that Mrs Quinn does not attempt to deal with Sheila's obvious abrasive personality. She would almost certainly have detected something in Sheila's manner which would lead her to suspect some deeper problem, but her experience would tell her that if this were the case then at some stage Sheila would probably come back.

The last point is that the interview takes place between two women. Why should this make a difference? Would it have been different if Sheila had been interviewed by a man?

Note

This study is based on a video-taped interview produced by the author for use in counselling training.

SETTING

The office of the Occupational Health Sister—Mrs Quinn.

PROBLEM

Mrs Quinn is waiting for a 'client' when there is a telephone call from Sheila Armstrong—a shorthand typist in the office of the Hospital Administrator.

S   1   *Mrs Quinn?, I'm Sheila Armstrong, I want to come and see you—now.* (Mrs Quinn had already had a hectic day and she felt herself becoming slightly annoyed by the imperious tone of Sheila but recognised that Sheila was upset.)

C   1   *You seem a bit upset Sheila, are you all right?*

S   2   *No I'm not all right; yes I am upset, that's why I want to see you.*

C   2   *I would like to see you now Sheila, but I will not be free for another hour, will that do?*

S   3   *Well I suppose it will have to; I'll be along sharp at four. Sheila arrived promptly at four, looking red-eyed and obviously angry. Before Mrs Quinn could say anything Sheila started.*

S   4   *That man! I could wring his neck. Look at my dress.* (She opened her coat to reveal some recent ink spots on her dress). *He did it, what my husband is going to say I don't know. He'll probably come up and throttle him. All this because he can't control his temper. I think I'll resign.* (With that she sat down, crossed one leg over the other, folded her arms and pouted at Mrs Quinn.)

C   4   *Oh dear, Sheila, I thought you were upset but you are really very angry.*

S   5   *Of course I'm angry, wouldn't you be?* (looking down at her dress.)

C   5   *Tell me exactly what happened.*

S   6   *Every day I go in to his office . . .*

C   6   *Do you mean Mr Miller, the Hospital Administrator?*

S   7   *Yes, the tyrant* (pause).

C   7   *Yes?*

S   8   (With obvious exasperation at being interrupted) *I go in every morning after coffee for him to dictate his letters and he's hopeless at it, he dictates far too fast and . . .*

155

C	8	*Something happened today when you went in, did it?*
S	9	*Usually I go in after coffee but today of all days, when I had so much to do, he was an hour late, an hour, mark you! (pause).*
C	9	*Yes?*
S	10	*Well, when he rang for me, I soon told him that I hadn't the time to do his letters; someone else would have to. I certainly didn't intend to be messed about like that.*
C	10	*Do you normally talk to your boss like that?*
S	11	*Now look here; it sounds as if you've been talking to him and made up your mind about me—have you?*
C	11	*Sheila, if you want me to try and help, you need to trust me. I have not been talking to Mr Miller about you and anything you say to me will not be repeated to him or anyone else. You strike me as being very unhappy and I want to try and help; please don't push me away by your anger. I know you are hurt about something, let's explore it together, shall we?*
S	12	*I'm sorry, Mrs Quinn, it was very rude of me. I did fly off the handle with Mr Miller but he needn't have done that, need he?*
C	12	*Did he really throw it at you; the ink, I mean?*
S	13	*(Smiling) No, he thumped the desk and his inkwell flew off and I just happened to be in the way.*
C	13	*He must have been very upset?*
S	14	*Yes he was furious. Funny, he gets like that a lot with me but not with the others. They all think he's fabulous.*
C	14	*Why do you think he gets upset with you and not with them?*
S	15	*Oh I expect they toady to him.*
C	15	*And you don't?*
S	16	*No, I call a spade a spade and speak my mind.*
C	16	*And Mr Miller resents this, does he?*
S	17	*From me he does, yet some of the others say he's a pleasant and good-natured man. Why does he pick on me?*
C	17	*Do you think you specially irritate him in some way?*
S	17	*My husband says it's because I'm bad-tempered.*

C   18   *Are you?*
S   19   *Yes, a lot of the time.*
C   19   *Are you bad-tempered especially with Mr Miller?*
S   20   *No, with everyone, I think. I fly off the handle so easily. I've always been like that and I think I probably make everyone in the office a bit touchy.*
C   20   *You feel you make life difficult for people, is that it?*
S   21   *I suppose I do and if I hadn't annoyed Mr Miller he wouldn't have knocked the ink over, would he?*
C   21   *It looks as if you owe him an apology, doesn't it?*
S   22   *Oh dear! I do hate apologies, I never admit that I am wrong. Could this be part of my problem, I wonder?*
C   22   *It certainly is difficult to work with people who are awkward to get along with, especially if they don't know when to say "sorry". Do you think you could start to look at how other people feel a bit more, it may help you to work better together?*
S   23   *Thank you Mrs Quinn, you've been a great help. Now I'll have to go and face Mr Miller.*

Sheila departed looking more relaxed than when she entered.

ANALYSIS OF INTERVIEW

This interview illustrates how the counsellor dealt firmly but empathetically with an obviously truculant young woman.

S   1   *It is often difficult to refuse an 'urgent' plea "can I come and see you now?" even though your reason for delay is genuine. Mrs Quinn did not respond to Sheila's asperity with annoyance although she did feel annoyed. This raises the question—how effectively can we disguise our feelings? Did Mrs Quinn's annoyance show through in her tone if not in her words?*
S   2   *Perhaps Sheila's tone in this section reflected some of the annoyance picked up from Mrs Quinn. Sheila seems the type of person who expects others to jump at her requests.*

S   4   *Sheila carries on as if there had never been a break from C 2. In the intervening hour her temper had not cooled. Mrs Quinn picks up non-verbal communication—appearance, crossed legs, folded arms and pouting.*

C   4   *Mrs Quinn's "You really are angry", again focussing on feelings, allows Sheila to ventilate a lot of negative feelings. Always listen carefully to negative feelings, they will tell you a great deal about attitudes.*

S   5   *Mrs Quinn ignores the leading question. Whether or not she would be angry is irrelevant. All Sheila wanted was for Mrs Quinn to take sides with her against her boss. She cuts through this and gets Sheila to relate exactly what happened.*

C   6   *Mrs Quinn interrupts Sheila in order to establish facts—who 'he' was. This interruption causes Sheila to have a break in her train of thought. Apart from Mrs Quinn wishing to establish clearly who 'he' was, she may have wished to teach Sheila a lesson in manners—to use a person's name. If this were the case it is likely that Sheila picked up the tone of censure which again caused her to pause.*

C   7   *Mrs Quinn's 'yes?' is really saying "do carry on". It is probable that she recognises Sheila's exasperation and does not wish to irritate her further. It is always a useful technique to say 'yes' or 'carry on' for it allows the person to choose how he does continue. A pause may indicate the end of a line of exploration, or coming up against a particularly sticky patch and not knowing quite how to put it over, or as in this case the thread of thought has been broken.*

C   8   *Mrs Quinn risks another interruption before Sheila has finished speaking. She could have allowed Sheila to continue to catalogue the faults of Mr Miller but it is doubtful if this would have been very productive. Her comment brings Sheila firmly back to the problem.*

S   9   *The pause here could have been an invitation to Mr Quinn to agree how awful Mr Miller's conduct was.*

C 10 *This comment by Mrs Quinn may have seemed out of place—calculated to increase antagonism. It really brings into focus the difference in approach according to the individual. She keeps Sheila firmly in touch with reality. It also highlights to Sheila that although Mrs Quinn is a 'helping person' that she too has standards of conduct and that if she questions what Sheila does other people probably do too.*

S 11 *Mrs Quinn has certainly jolted Sheila. Now the centre of attention moves from the action between Sheila and Mr Miller to what is happening between Sheila and Mrs Quinn.*

C 11 *One gets the impression that this section is the turning point, the fulcrum of the whole interview; that everything depends upon what Mrs Quinn says. She does not fall into the trap of saying that everything Sheila says will be confidential before she has heard all the facts. She may, at some stage, have to go to Mr Miller and say that Sheila has approached her—the details of the interview with Sheila would, of course, be confidential. She may, on the other hand, not see it as part of her role to speak to Mr Miller—she may see her work as being directly and exclusively with Sheila. But if the situation did not improve it may be necessary to involve him.*

Mrs Quinn's humanity comes through and it is this which seems to penetrate and get behind the anger, particularly the sentence, "You strike me as being very unhappy . . ."

The words ". . . push me away . . ." imply a physical action, and could have helped Sheila to see that she was physically rejecting someone who was trying to help.

Her "I know you are hurt . . ." shows Sheila that Mrs Quinn understands that a great deal of pain underlies the anger, and that in all probability it goes deeper than this single incident. Her "Let's explore this together . . ." demonstrates that if Sheila is to be helped, she has to work at it—that she and Mrs Quinn together, and not Mrs Quinn alone, is the answer.

It is possible that Sheila's words at the beginning of S 11 hurt Mrs Quinn, and some of that came through; it was this which touched Sheila and brought her near to tears.

Some people assert that the counsellor must never show his feelings, they will get in the way of objectivity. This is difficult if not impossible, to achieve and it is questionable whether such a passive, all-accepting attitude is helpful to the client. This is the concept of the 'sounding board'—someone who merely reflects back the feelings of the other person.

Another point of view is that clients respond better to reality. If reality is that the counsellor is hurt (or pleased) by what is said or done, and this feeling is conveyed to the client, he will have something positive by which to modify his own responses. He may thus use the experiences within the counselling relationship as a platform upon which to stand and test other relationships.

This does not mean that the counsellor reacts to everything the client says in the way that someone might who is inexperienced in the ways of counselling. The responses of the counsellor spring from the wells of understanding—of himself and of other people. This understanding makes it less likely for his reactions to hurt the client; his aim is to encourage the client to think and explore further and more deeply his own reactions.

S   12   Sheila responds to Mrs Quinn in a positive manner. Is she really saying "I flew off the handle with you too"?

C   12   Again Mrs Quinn side-stepped the invitation to condemn Mr Miller. She seems to be deliberately introducing humour here. This could be an unconscious tension-release mechanism—something to balance the emotion of the previous exchange. It worked!

C   13   Here Mrs Quinn focusses Sheila's attention on how Mr Miller must have felt. The timing of this movement is important. It is doubtful if she could have

160

introduced this any earlier in the interview. Before S 11, Sheila was too preoccupied with her own feelings to consider those of anyone else. Now she is in a different position. The rapport which has been established between them enables her to think about her own behaviour and its consequences.

C 14 *Mrs Quinn is trying to get Sheila to look objectively at her part in the interaction with Mr Miller.*

S 15 *Sheila here seems to be expressing some regret; even although she disparages the others she probably secretly wishes she too could be on good terms with her boss.*

C 15 *The whole of this section shows how Mrs Quinn keeps Sheila moving towards insight by helping her to see that Mr Miller is responding to the way she acts.*

S 18 *It is in the sentence "My husband . . ." that she finally admits the fault. She goes on to say that she is bad-tempered with everyone—quite an admission!*

C 20 *Mrs Quinn is not satisfied, however, and pushes home one more point—that she makes life difficult for 'people'; not just Mr Miller.*

S 21 *The last bit of the jigsaw has fallen into place with the admission that the ink stains on her dress were really an outcome of her own behaviour.*

C 21 *Not everyone would have suggested that Sheila should apologise, but Mrs Quinn knew her client and probably recognised that she needed firm handling. She puts the responsibility fairly on Sheila for her actions.*

S 22 *From Mrs Quinn's response, Sheila develops a little more insight as she questions the fact that she finds it difficult to admit that she is ever wrong.*

C 22 *Mrs Quinn leaves Sheila with some 'homework'—to examine how she gets along with people and to consider their feelings a bit more.*

Sheila left Mrs Quinn's office more relaxed than when she came in and her anger had been replaced with a degree of insight. She had not been left in any doubt as to her part in the affair and what she could do to try to put matters right.

SUMMARY OF SHEILA ARMSTRONG

Mrs Quinn's style of interviewing is different from that of Andy Jones, but they both dealt with anger and hostility in much the same way and achieved much the same result—a lowering of the emotional tone.

She is much more direct in her approach than Andy was, but she ably dealt with Sheila and helps her to look at the way she relates to people.

Some months later Mrs Quinn received another telephone call from Sheila; this time she requested an appointment ". . . when it is convenient; there is something very special and personal I would like to discuss with you." This 'problem' (to be the subject of a case study some time in the future) turned out to be that she desperately wanted children but, although she had been married six years, had not been successful. This peep into the future shows that underlying Sheila's irascible behaviour (and possibly directly linked to it), was a far more serious and deeper personal difficulty.

THE CASE OF ANNE DUKE

This case study, centred around a school, is applicable, in many respects, to any work situation. I leave you to make the link between this and your own organisation.

Anne Duke is a chemistry teacher in a London school. Over the past five years she has had increasing problems with her eyesight; she has been very secretive about the exact diagnosis. The headmistress has frequently had to find a replacement for Anne when she was attending the hospital for treatment. She also feels that Anne is becoming an increasing hazard in the laboratory. She would drop things and not be able to see them, blunder into desks and chairs and had obvious difficulty reading labels on bottles and jars. Correcting homework, Miss Windspear often thought, must be a nightmare. She had discussed the situation with Anne who firmly insisted that she could manage perfectly well, but it was patently obvious that she was not able to carry out her duties efficiently. Miss Windspear discussed the problem with the Assistant Chief Education Officer who arranged to see Anne in Miss Windspear's Office.

Mr Spence discovered that Anne, a spinster, lived on her own in a large third-floor flat in an old Victorian house, six miles from the school. There were three other flats in the house, all occupied by young couples with children. She had her own kitchen, bath and toilet facilities. It was an all-electric flat for which she paid about a quarter of her salary each month in rent.

She had lived there for ten years since losing both her parents, with whom she had lived until they died. She had one brother, ten years older than she, who lived in Scotland. He did not enjoy good health since a shooting accident during the war when he had to have his leg amputated. He had suggested that he and Anne set up home together in Scotland. Anne did not like the idea; she was not due to retire for another five years and did not relish the thought of retiring now and keeping home for her brother. She knew she could not find a new job at her age.

She travelled the six miles to the school by a combination of walking, underground train and bus; the return journey added two hours to her working day. When she spoke about her eyesight, Mr Spence felt she was not being realistic. The eye specialist had not been able to give her any firm conclusion—only that the condition was progressive and inoperable. Mr Spence put it to Anne that perhaps she ought to consider a premature retirement on health grounds, but she resisted this suggestion.

ANALYSIS

Anne has five years to serve before she can retire under normal arrangements. What will it mean to her to retire at 55? Think of this from the following aspects:

A: loss of identity;
B: colleagues and pupils;
C: financial;
D: housing.

A.   As a chemistry teacher she has a certain standing and status, not only in the school but in the community. If she retires, she will become a 'retired' schoolteacher. What is this likely to mean to her? Will she feel she is being thrown on the scrap heap?

B.   Her handicap must have already started to curtail her contact with people because of decreased mobility. If her colleagues and pupils are removed, her world will shrink. Will she be able to compensate? What outside activities does she have which will allow her world to expand in a different direction? A person who spends her whole life as a teacher is likely to experience a dramatic emptiness when deprived of contact with her pupils.

C.   What would her financial position be if she could no longer work? Would she receive a pension from the Education Department? Would she receive financial assistance from Social Security? Would she receive any form of Invalidity Pension? She would not receive the Old Age Pension until age 60.

D.   If she retired prematurely could she afford to continue living where she now lives? How much longer can she continue living there anyway? Are there specific factors which become hazardous as her condition deteriorates? Do children leave toys on the stairs, for instance? If she retires and continues living there, could she become isolated?

Many people postpone any preparation for retirement, but at least they know when the axe will fall; for Anne, the future seems to have caught up with her before time. What can be done?

From a management point of view the headmistress is probably right that Anne has become a liability, and Mr Spence is equally right that she should retire. From a

164

humanitarian point of view I'm sure both Miss Windspear and Mr Spence find themselves on the horns of a dilemma. Managers frequently find themselves faced with two opposing and irreconcilable factors—the person versus the organisation.

The manager must weigh up the pros and cons *then make a decision*. To make a decision without a careful study of *all* the factors would not be good management; neither would it be good management to study the pros and cons and not make a decision. Nothing is more soul-destroying than the manager who cannot make a decision because someone might be hurt. In this case Mr Spence had several discussions with his own boss, their legal adviser and Miss Windspear. The following plan was agreed.

THE PLAN

1. Anne would be retired with pension in six months' time which would include the Summer holiday. She would return to work for a month after that holiday to help orientate the chemistry teacher whom they hoped they would be able to appoint in time. She would also receive six months' pay when she left.
2. Mr Spence would see her if necessary, but would leave Miss Windspear to tell her. When she had told Anne of the decision, the Chief Education Officer would write officially, laying out the terms, including details of her pension.
3. The Welfare Officer would be asked to contact Anne with a view to offering emotional support through counselling.

THE ACTION

When Miss Windspear told Anne, she was distressed but did not create a scene. She told Miss Windspear that she was relieved that the decision had been taken out of her hands and that, had it been left to her, she would not have been able to make up her mind.

Miss Windspear and Anne drafted an advertisement for the replacement teacher, then they started making plans for the change-over. Miss Windspear suggested that she would like her to help with the selection and interviewing of the candidates. Anne agreed to this.

The Education Authority, having made the decision that Anne would be retired, have done all they could to be fair; fair to the organisation and to Anne. Not only have they done what is administratively correct, but also what is humane. They have recognised, in spite of the financial arrangements, which are obviously important, that Anne may have personal adjustments to make which the welfare officer could possibly help her to tackle.

Mr Smart, as a frequent visitor to the school, knew Anne by sight and agreed to help if he could. He contacted Anne one day in the staff room and was quite direct in his approach: was there anything he could do to help? At first Anne was reluctant to talk about it, but he persisted and over the next few months was able to help her in many ways.

She was able to talk about her many fears: loneliness, financial hardship, decreased mobility and eventual blindness. By getting her to talk about her blindness he was able to introduce her to a social work colleague who worked with blind clients in Anne's locality.

As the time for retirement drew near, just before the holidays, the social worker spent more time with Anne and introduced her to a club for the partially-sighted near where Anne lived.

During the holidays this club was a great support to her. The social worker made sure that Anne told her G.P. what was happening, which was a wise precaution for in the weeks following retirement, Anne passed through a period of depression which slowly passed. The social worker and the welfare officer continued to visit Anne for some time after her depression lifted. When they were convinced she was coping, the welfare officer ceased visiting and the social worker gradually established a regular visiting routine as Anne became more independent in her new life.

This case illustrates the importance of harnessing the services of other people—the welfare officer and social worker. Mr Spence, because he felt sorry for Anne, could have refused to back Miss Windspear and left Anne in the post for another five years. This could have resulted in a lowering of morale within the school; accidents could have occurred, which might have involved pupils and could possibly have resulted in litigation. In addition, such a course of action would not have been helpful to Anne. She would not have been any better prepared for retirement than she was, and if her eyesight had deteriorated much more, a decision would have been forced on them. A forced decision often results in hasty action, which might have been to Anne's disadvantage. It is just possible that she could have been found another job within the school for five years.

What do you think?

What would you have done?

Look at how Miss Windspear handled the situation after the decision had been made.

THE CASE OF MARY SMITH

Mary, aged 19, came to a large American computer firm as a temporary secretary and was asked by the Sales Manager to stay on permanently to help him set up a new branch of the business.

There were three male management personnel and seven salesmen involved. She was given free rein in all departments and was actively encouraged to set up her own systems. Due to the volume of work and the fact that everything was running at high pressure, she became unable to cope, and started to work from twelve to thirteen hours a day. Gradually she became exhausted and began moving slowly and dreamily; she would cry when more work was given to her. As a side issue, a kidney infection necessitated her visiting the toilet more frequently than usual.

The situation went on for about six weeks until the Sales Manager called her into his office and the following took place.

Sales Manager
Mary, come in and sit down. We're worried about you because we know you're taking drugs.

Mary
I certainly am not; what on earth makes you say that?

Sales Manager
Now come on Mary, we know you are, and of course you can't do this job under these circumstances, can you? I know the work has been very heavy and we've all been under pressure, starting up this outfit, but it's more than just that with you. Why don't you get some help?

Mary *(furious)*
I repeat, I have not taken any drugs and never will. I was under the impression that you asked me to stay permanently to help you set up this thing and that more staff would be provided. Instead, I've been working twelve hours a day and I'm exhausted. And all you have provided is one junior who can hardly type.

Sales Manager *(becoming angry)*
And if you didn't spend so much time in the Ladies, combing your hair, you'd be better off. You were in there five times this morning. But we know that's to do with the drugs.

Mary
I'm going to see the Personnel Manager and get my cards and I'm going. Thank you Mr . . . for your help!

Sales Manager
I'm sorry you've taken it like this Mary. You can stay for a week or so.

Mary
I'm going—now.

She left the company that afternoon.

ANALYSIS

This case illustrates several points.

168

1.   *Management was at fault somewhere if anyone, particularly a young person of 19, was working 12 hours a day, and the fact passed unobserved. Or, if it were observed, the significance was not taken account of in assessing her performance and behaviour.*

2.   *The Sales Manager did some fact-gathering, and it was true that Mary had been visiting the Ladies frequently, but a completely wrong interpretation had been made. This illustrates the danger of confusing facts with opinions. It may be true that Mary's behaviour was similar to that of someone on drugs, but opinion is not enough.*

3.   *The Sales Manager and all the other staff were working under pressure. In such circumstances it is natural for tempers to fray; frayed tempers are not conducive to effective counselling.*

4.   *This manager certainly believes in getting straight to the point and it is possible that such an attack, in the right circumstances (if Mary had been on drugs) could have worked, (based, no doubt on shock tactics). In this instance he was off target.*

   He could have extricated himself by a simple "Sorry Mary, tell me what is the matter". He seemed unable to cope with Mary's anger—he responded to it by becoming angry himself. The result was an upward spiral of heightened emotion and one efficient secretary lost to the company.

How would you tackle this?

THE CASE OF DENNIS GOODLAD

Dennis, aged 40, has been employed as a storekeeper in a large District Hospital for 2 years. George Matthews, aged 55, the District Supplies Manager, was appointed three months previously on retirement from the Supplies Section of the R.A.F.

Shortly after he arrived, George noticed that Dennis spent a great deal of time in the staff room, and frequently during the day his breath smelled of alcohol. George made a casual inspection of the staff room but could find no evidence of alcohol. George was particularly sensitive to the smell as he himself was strictly teetotal.

On Christmas Eve, George came back from his lunch to discover that Dennis had not returned. He asked several of the other men but they hadn't seen him either. An hour later Dennis arrived, bleary-eyed and smelling strongly of drink but not actually incapable.

George listened to his reason for being late; he had been invited to a party in one of the other departments and hadn't noticed the time. He offered to work late that evening to make up; he seemed very contrite. Because it was Christmas, George didn't wish to be too hard but told Dennis that he didn't expect this behaviour and hoped that it would not happen again. He told his staff that as far as he was concerned he did not approve of drinking alcohol on duty, and no provision had been made for a departmental party.

Over the Christmas holiday George had a coronary attack and was away three months. During this time his Deputy kept the department running. When George returned, he seemed quite fit and everyone rallied round to help him. About two weeks later he went into the staff room and found Dennis's locker open and in it an empty whisky bottle. A few days later he was walking round the hospital when he saw Dennis come out of a disused building. Later that day he again smelled of alcohol. He spoke to his Deputy who said he had noticed nothing unusual during the time George was away ill.

One Saturday morning George was telephoned at home by the shift supervisor to say that Dennis, who had been in, could not be found anywhere. He was particularly annoyed because he was already short-staffed as one of the other men had rung in to say he was ill.

George went down to the hospital, had a word with the supervisor, found that he was coping well then went to look at the disused building. There he found Dennis and two other men, whom he didn't know, having a drinking session.

170

On his way up he had been telling himself not to get angry, for he knew this would not help his blood pressure.

He asked the other men who they were, and as they were not employed in the hospital he ordered them off the premises and told Dennis to get back to the Stores and get on with his work. He contacted Security and told them of the incident. He told the supervisor what had happened and said he would deal with it on Monday.

On Monday morning he sent for Dennis and told him there was no option but to issue a written warning, that he was lucky not to be dismissed on the spot, and that his performance would be kept under strict observation. He then put all the facts down in Dennis' file.

The following day he called Dennis in, asked him to sit down and suggested that it might help if they could talk about what appeared to be a problem. Dennis apologised profusely and repeatedly vowed that it would not happen again. George found himself becoming frustrated and annoyed; he couldn't seem to get to grips with Dennis at all. He realised that he could do himself more harm than good trying to help Dennis, so he rang the Personnel Manager who sent Bill, one of his staff, to assist.

George left most of the talking to Bill, and after about an hour all they could discover was that Dennis lived with his aged and rapidly deteriorating mother who needed constant attention. Bill contacted the Social Services who a few days later, sent a social worker to discuss possible arrangements for Dennis' mother. Dennis was worried what would happen to him when she eventually died.

Bill tried to get him to look at what appeared to be a drink problem, but Dennis hotly protested that it was not a problem. "I'm not an alcoholic, if that's what you think; I just like a few." There seemed very little more which could be done at this stage.

George spoke to his Deputy, who admitted that there had been one or two occasions during George's illness when he thought Dennis was acting a bit strangely, but he had been too busy to investigate and yes, it could have been drink. George spoke to the two supervisors and explained the situation to them.

171

Bill, *from Personnel, George and his Deputy tried at different times to get Dennis to talk about himself, but repeatedly he avowed there was nothing to worry about. His appearance began to deteriorate and he became more withdrawn. No-one actually caught him drinking and George particularly felt they could be in danger of witch-hunting.*

This came to a head one day about three months after the last incident. The staff arrived on duty one morning to find Dennis already in the staff room, dead drunk and totally incapable of carrying out his duties. He had apparently slipped unobserved into the staff room at the end of the previous day, and had remained there all night drinking from a supply of liquor in his locker.

George, in the presence of his Deputy, dismissed Dennis on the spot, telephoned Bill to tell him what had happened and arranged for a taxi to take Dennis home, accompanied by one of the supervisors. He then sat down and made a full written report to the District Administrator.

ANALYSIS

This case study has been included to show that sometimes counselling is not appropriate; that it does not solve all problems and the only course left is discipline.

In this instance it is very doubtful if George, Bill, or anyone else, could have done more than they did. I'm certain that George, particularly, felt unhappy about sacking Dennis, but could he have done anything else?

We still do not know for certain that Dennis was an alcoholic, but it would certainly seem this way. George or Bill could have contacted Alcoholics Anonymous; they may have been able to offer assistance. Perhaps being sacked will show Dennis that he is at the bottom of the well. When he realises this (if he does) he can do one of two things: stay there or ask for help and with the support of (for instance) A.A. start the long climb upwards.

From a management point of view George stuck to the rules; could he be criticised in any way? Although it was never discussed, it is almost certain that Dennis' drinking had been going on before George came. If this is so, should it have been dealt with before? There is also the fact that the Deputy was not as discerning as George of Dennis' behaviour.

What influence did George's coronary have on the way he handled Dennis? Do you feel he was fair in the way he handled the situation that Saturday morning? What would have happened if he had dismissed him then?

George's attempts at counselling did not achieve much. Should he have involved the Personnel Department at this stage, or should he have kept it within his own department? Can you think of any other way you would have tried to help Dennis?

George was particularly sensitive to the fact that, because of his own approach to alcohol, he could be accused of witch-hunting. Do you think this was the case? Do you think he was pursuing Dennis? In spite of the fact that he had just sacked Dennis he was humanitarian enough to provide a taxi home with an escort.

This whole case raises the question of one's attitude towards alcohol. George states his policy of 'no drinking on duty' and one can see a certain logic in this. We do not know the reasons for his total abstinence but whatever they were they must have been strong if he retained his position through a Service career. What possible reasons could you think of? Could he, for example, be an ex-alcoholic?

The question must be asked about your own attitude towards alcoholism. Do you regard it as an illness comparable with, say, diabetes (which may render a person unfit for duty) or even with George's coronary, or do you regard it as a self-inflicted condition? The same two-part question could be asked of drug-taking.

I do not propose to explore the ins and outs of these two opposing viewpoints, but simply to draw your attention to them and hope you will clarify your own thinking. What you believe will determine your attitude towards members of your staff who are, or may become, alcoholics.

TERMINATION

This stage of the book is approached with a mixture of regret and relief—regret that some of the ideas and concepts have not emerged as lucidly as I thought they would, and perhaps as a result you have been left puzzled and confused. The relief comes from the knowledge that my struggle to make sense of what I wanted to say is nearly over, but this relief is tinged with a certain sadness which is difficult to analyse.

It is similar to how Andy felt when his counselling relationship with Tom ended. Much had happened; they had both experienced struggles, and the development which had taken place within the one had been sparked off by the other. I have been conscious during this time of writing that fresh revelation has come to me as I have grappled with my ideas and theories.

My two-part aim was to show that counselling is an essential management skill and to develop some principles which can be used by anyone in whatever sphere of work. I have emphasised throughout that counselling is a subtle blend of learning and experience. Many questions have deliberately been left open-ended and vague, because there is no one answer which would suit every case. I may not have been able to provide many answers but I'm certain you will have been provoked and encouraged to ask many questions; about your own personality and how it influences your counselling.

Counselling deals with feelings as well as with facts, and counselling development must be concerned as much with personality development as with theory. Generally speaking, we experience less difficulty with facts than with feelings, and what I have tried to do is to look beyond the superficial to what lies beneath; to explore the emotions and motives of the person which have given rise to some problem. In the process of looking at what lies beneath the skin of others we are forced to acknowledge that much of what we see is present in ourselves.

If we are to develop our counselling skill we must submit ourselves to a constant appraisal and reappraisal of how we counsel, in whatever sphere of work we are engaged, and whether the counselling is related to personal problems or performance.

READING LIST

The majority of books include a reading list or bibliography. Whilst there are some benefits to be obtained from such lists, I personally feel that so often the references are already outdated by the time the new book is published. A far more useful way is to use the 'enquire within' system operating in any reference library. Almost at a glance one can discover all books in print on, in this instance, counselling.

What I *have* done is to provide a few names and addresses where further details of counselling literature can be obtained.

1. *Counselling and Guidance* published by the National Book League, 7 Albemarle Street, London W1X 4BB. An annotated list of various counselling books.
2. The British Association for Counselling, 1a Little Church Street, Rugby. An organisation run *by* counsellors *for* counsellors.
3. *British Journal of Guidance and Counselling,* published by the Careers Research and Advisory Centre, Bateman Street, Cambridge CB2 1LZ.
4. *New Society,* published weekly.
5. *Social Work Today,* published by the British Association of Social Work.
6. The National Marriage Guidance Council, Little Church Street, Rugby, Warwickshire.